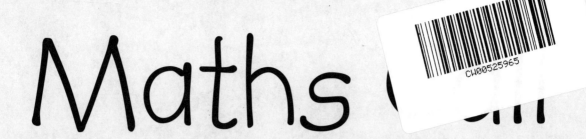

Maths Chant

Developing children's
listening skills in the
Daily Maths Lesson

YEAR
6

Peter Clarke

Published by Collins Educational
An imprint of HarperCollins*Publishers* Ltd
77-85 Fulham Palace Road
Hammersmith
London
W6 8JB

www.**Collins**Education.com
On-line Support for Schools and Colleges

First published 2002

ISBN 0 00 713356 1

Cover design by Caroline Grimshaw
Cover illustration by Andrew Hamilton
Series design by Neil Adams
Illustrations by Bethan Matthews, Jeffrey Reid, Lisa Williams, Mel Sharp, Rhiannon Powell.

Printed by Martins the Printers, Berwick on Tweed

Contents

Introduction

Maths Call is a series of seven books from Reception to Year 6 which is designed to assist children to practise and consolidate objectives from the National Numeracy Strategy (NNS) *Framework for Teaching Mathematics* at the same time as developing their listening skills.

Listening and following instructions are two key skills that are crucial to the success of every child and every adult. How many times have children had to redo work because they have not listened to your directions? How many times do you have to repeat yourself? How often have you wished you could take time out from the overburdened curriculum to help children develop their listening skills? This series will help you solve these problems. You will not have to take time away from other curriculum areas to do this since *Maths Call* helps to develop children's listening skills and ability to follow oral directions while they practise valuable mathematical skills.

Listening and communicating

The purpose of this book is the development of children's listening skills through the mathematics curriculum, but this skill is not seen in isolation. Many of the activities outlined include reading, speaking and writing. Listening is an integral part of communication which deals with the process of giving and receiving information. The four different aspects of the communication process outlined below rely upon each other for effective communication at the same time as actively supporting and enriching one another.

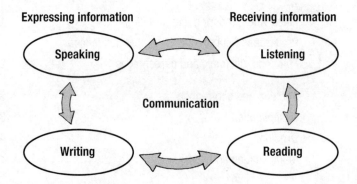

Communication and mental imagery

All children, whatever their age and ability, have their own mental images, developed from previous knowledge and experiences. Aural stimulus enables children to manipulate the mental images they have of numbers, shapes and measures. Instant recall of number facts such as the multiplication tables and the addition and subtraction number facts often depends on an aural input. Children have to hear the sounds in order to give an automatic response.

The difficult part for the teacher is to discover what is going on inside children's heads. This is where discussion as an accompaniment to mental work is so important. It is only through discussion that the teacher can begin to develop an insight into children's mental processes. Discussions also enable children to develop their own insights into their mental imagery and provide the opportunity for them to share their ideas and methods. They can form judgements about the alternatives, decide which methods are the most efficient and effective for them, and further develop flexibility and familiarity with the different mathematical topics.

The skills of listening

Listening skills can be improved through training and practice. When direct attention is paid to listening for specific purposes, and these skills are practised and consolidated, improvement in ability follows. In general children tend to learn and remember more through listening than in almost any other way. A high percentage of all the information children receive comes through their ears. Thus direct training in the skills of listening can be hugely beneficial to all learning.

Effective listening involves:
- hearing
- concentrating
- a knowledge of language
- a knowledge of the structure of language
- recognising cues
- being able to contextualise
- inferring
- thinking
- processing
- summarising
- selecting
- organising
- drawing upon previous knowledge and experience
- comprehending/understanding the main idea.

Becoming a good listener

Display the poster on page 6 to remind children of how to become a good listener. When concentrating on developing children's listening skills draw attention to the poster.

Characteristics of a good listener

A good listener is one who:
- knows how to listen
- is able to concentrate on listening
- looks at the speaker
- is courteous to the speaker
- does not interrupt the speaker
- is able to zero in on the speaker and eliminate extraneous noises and interruptions
- can comprehend
- is selective
- asks him/herself questions while listening
- draws upon their previous knowledge and experiences
- evaluates while listening
- remembers what is said
- anticipates what is coming next.

Good listening

Sit still

Think about the words

Look at the speaker

Maths Call and the teaching–learning cycle

Assessment

- Each activity can be used to assess a specific objective from the NNS *Framework*.
- Guidance given on how to record pupil performance.

Planning

- Each activity linked to an objective in the NNS *Framework*.
- Guidance given for planning a programme of work.

Teaching

- Clear and complete instructions given for each activity.
- Ideally suited to the daily mathematics lesson.

Curriculum information

Each of the 30 activities is organised under specific objectives as identified in the NNS *Framework*. The *Maths Call* objectives coverage chart on pages 8 and 9 shows which activity is matched to which objective(s).

Planning a programme of work for *Maths Call*

The *Maths Call* programme chart on page 10 may be used in conjunction with your long- and medium-term plans to develop a *Maths Call* programme of work throughout the year. By following the topics allocated using the NNS *Framework* or a similar scheme of work you will ensure that the children have the opportunity to practise and consolidate the topic, and specific objectives for a particular week, at the same time as developing their listening skills.

Maths Call and the daily mathematics lesson

The activities contained in *Maths Call* are ideally suited to the daily mathematics lesson. Each activity is designed to be presented to the whole class. The activities are extremely flexible and can be used in a variety of ways. For example, activities can be used during the:

- oral work and mental calculation session to practise and consolidate previously taught concepts;
- main teaching part of the lesson to focus on particular skills and concepts;
- plenary session to consolidate the concept(s) taught during the main part of the lesson and to conclude the lesson in an enjoyable way.

Maths Call objectives coverage

STRAND	TOPIC	OBJECTIVES	ACTIVITY	PAGE
Numbers and the number system	Place value, ordering and rounding	Multiply and divide decimals mentally by 10 or 100, and integers by 1000, and explain the effect.	1	12
		Find the difference between a positive and a negative integer, or two negative integers, in a context such as temperature or the number line, and order a set of positive and negative integers.	2	14
	Properties of numbers and number sequences	Recognise and extend number sequences, such as the sequence of square numbers, or the sequence of triangular numbers 1, 3, 6, 10, 15...	3	16
		Find simple common multiples. Recognise squares of numbers to at least 12×12. Recognise prime numbers to at least 20. Factorise numbers to 100 into prime factors.	4	18
	Fractions, decimals and percentages	Change a fraction such as $\frac{33}{8}$ to the equivalent mixed number $4\frac{1}{8}$, and vice versa. Reduce a fraction to its simplest form by cancelling common factors in the numerator and denominator. Order fractions such as $\frac{2}{3}$, $\frac{3}{4}$ and $\frac{5}{6}$ by converting them to fractions with a common denominator, and position them on a number line.	5	20
		Use a fraction as an 'operator' to find fractions, including tenths and hundredths, of numbers or quantities (e.g. $\frac{5}{8}$ of 32, $\frac{7}{10}$ of 40, $\frac{9}{100}$ of 400 centimetres).	6	22
		Know what each digit represents in a number with up to three decimal places. Give a decimal fraction lying between two others (e.g. between 3.4 and 3.5). Order a mixed set of numbers or measurements with up to three decimal places. Round a number with two decimal places to the nearest tenth or to the nearest whole number.	7	24
		Recognise the equivalence between the decimal and fraction forms of one half, one quarter, three quarters, one eighth... and tenths, hundredths and thousandths (e.g. $\frac{700}{1000} = \frac{70}{100} = \frac{7}{10} = 0.7$).	8	26
		Express simple fractions such as one half, one quarter, three quarters, one third, two thirds..., and tenths and hundredths, as percentages (e.g. know that $\frac{1}{3} = 33\frac{1}{3}\%$). Find simple percentages of small whole-number quantities (e.g. find 10% of £500, then 20%, 40% and 80% by doubling).	9	28
Calculations	Addition and subtraction	Use known number facts and place value to consolidate mental addition/subtraction.	10	30
		Use informal pencil and paper methods to support, record or explain additions and subtractions. Extend written methods to column addition and subtraction of numbers involving decimals.	11	32
	Multiplication	Consolidate knowing by heart multiplication facts up to 10×10.	12	34
		Use informal pencil and paper methods to support, record or explain multiplications. Extend written methods to multiplication of ThHTU $\times$ U (short multiplication).	13	36
		Use informal pencil and paper methods to support, record or explain multiplications. Extend written methods to short multiplication of numbers involving decimals.	14	38
		Use informal pencil and paper methods to support, record or explain multiplications. Extend written methods to long multiplication of a three-digit by a two-digit integer.	15	40

STRAND	TOPIC	OBJECTIVES	ACTIVITY	PAGE
Calculations *continued*	Division	Use informal pencil and paper methods to support, record or explain divisions. Extend written methods to short division of TU or HTU by U (mixed-number answer).	16	42
		Use informal pencil and paper methods to support, record or explain divisions. Extend written methods to division of HTU by TU (long division, whole-number answer).	17	44
		Use informal pencil and paper methods to support, record or explain divisions. Extend written methods to short division of numbers involving decimals.	18	46
	Multiplication and division	Derive quickly: – division facts corresponding to tables up to 10×10; – squares of multiples of 10 to 100 (e.g. 60×60); – doubles of two-digit numbers (e.g. 3.8×2, 0.76×2); – doubles of multiples of 10 to 1000 (e.g. 670×2); – doubles of multiples of 100 to 10 000 (e.g. 6500×2); – and the corresponding halves.	19	48
		Use known number facts and place value to consolidate mental multiplication and division.	20	50
Solving problems	Problems involving 'real life' and measures	Identify and use appropriate operations (including combinations of operations) to solve word problems involving numbers and quantities based on 'real life' and measures (including time), using one or more steps. Explain methods and reasoning.	21	52
	Problems involving money	Identify and use appropriate operations (including combinations of operations) to solve word problems involving numbers and quantities based on money using one or more steps, including converting pounds to foreign currency, or vice versa, and calculating percentages such as VAT. Explain methods and reasoning.	22	54
Measures	Length, mass and capacity	Use, read and write standard metric units (km, m, cm, mm, kg, g, l, ml, cl), including their abbreviations, and relationships between them. Convert larger to smaller units (e.g. m to km, cm or mm to m, g to kg, ml to l) and vice versa. Know imperial units (mile, pint, gallon, lb, oz). Know rough equivalents of lb and kg, oz and g, miles and km, litres and pints or gallons.	23	56
	Area and perimeter	Calculate the perimeter and area of simple compound shapes that can be split into rectangles.	24	58
	Time	Appreciate different times around the world.	25	60
Shape and space	3-D and 2-D shapes	Describe and visualise properties of solid shapes such as parallel or perpendicular faces or edges. Classify quadrilaterals, using criteria such as parallel sides, equal angles, equal sides...	26	62
	Translation	Recognise where a shape will be after two translations.	27	64
	Position and direction	Read and plot co-ordinates in all four quadrants.	28	66
	Angle and rotation	Use a protractor to measure and draw acute and obtuse angles to the nearest degree.	29	68
Handling data	Handling data	Solve a problem by representing, extracting and interpreting data in bar charts with grouped discrete data.	30	70

Maths Call programme

| YEAR |
| CLASS |
| TEACHER |

	WEEK	TOPIC	*MATHS CALL* ACTIVITY
AUTUMN	1		
	2		
	3		
	4		
	5		
	6		
	7		
	8		
	9		
	10		
	11		
	12		
SPRING	1		
	2		
	3		
	4		
	5		
	6		
	7		
	8		
	9		
	10		
	11		
	12		
SUMMER	1		
	2		
	3		
	4		
	5		
	6		
	7		
	8		
	9		
	10		
	11		
	12		

How to use *Maths Call*

Preparation

- Provide each child with the necessary resources. These are listed at the beginning of each activity's teacher's page.

Instructions

Explain the following to the children:
- They need to listen carefully.
- They will be given some oral instructions to follow.
- The instructions will only be given once.
- They must only do what they are told to do, nothing more.
- They may not use an eraser.
- How many instructions there are for the particular activity.
- That they are to do each task immediately after the instructions for that part have been given.

The activity

- If necessary, briefly discuss the pupil sheet with the children. Ensure that the children are familiar with the pictures and/or the text on the sheet.
- Ensure that the children are also familiar with any of the terms used in the oral instructions. Refer to the *Key words* for a list of the relevant vocabulary.
- Ask the children to write the date on the sheet in the space provided.
- Do not ask the children to write their name. This will occur during the activity.
- Slowly read the instructions to the children.

Discussion

- After the children have completed the sheet, discuss the activity with the class. You may decide to do this either before or after marking the activity. Use the *Discussion questions* as a springboard. For each activity there are questions that have been designed to cater for higher attaining (↑) and lower attaining (↓) pupils.

Marking

- Mark the sheet with the whole class, either before or after the discussion. You may wish the children to mark their own sheet or to swap with someone next to them. However, if you are using the activity as an assessment tool then you may decide to mark the sheets yourself at a later stage.

Revisiting an activity

- Repeat an activity with the class at a later stage in the year. Children can compare how they performed on the task the second time round.
- You may like to alter the activity slightly by changing one or two of the instructions.

Maths Call and assessment

Maths Call activities may be used with the whole class or with groups of children as an assessment activity. Linked to the topic that is being studied at present, *Maths Call* will provide you with an indication of how well the children have understood the objectives being covered as well as how their listening skills are developing. The *Maths Call* assessment sheet on page 72 may be used to record how well the children have understood the objectives covered in the activity.

Place value, ordering and rounding

■ Multiply and divide decimals mentally by 10 or 100, and integers by 1000, and explain the effect.

Resources

Provide each child with the following:
■ a copy of Activity 1 pupil sheet
■ a pencil

Key words

zero, one, two…one million   decimal   point   integer   multiply
multiplied by   times   divide   divided by

Say to the children:

Listen carefully.

I am going to tell you some things to do.

I will say them only once, so listen very carefully.

Do only the things you are told to do and nothing else.

If you make a mistake, cross it out. Do not use an eraser.

There are 16 parts to this activity.

The activity

1. Find the number 37.47. What is 37.47 divided by 100? Write the answer on the book.

2. Find the number 42. What is 42 multiplied by 1000? Write the answer on the book.

3. Find the number 5.6. What is 5.6 times 10? Write the answer on the book.

4. Find the number 9.45. What is 9.45 divided by 10? Write the answer on the book.

5. Find the number 4.34. What is 4.34 multiplied by 100? Write the answer on the book.

6. Find the number 22.61. What is 22.61 divided by 10? Write the answer on the book.

7. Find the number 6.24. What is 6.24 multiplied by 10? Write the answer on the book.

8. Find the number 5.62. What is 5.62 divided by 100? Write the answer on the book.

9. Find the number 79 340. What is 79340 divided by 1000? Write the answer on the book.

10. Find the number 8.7. What is 8.7 multiplied by 100? Write the answer on the book.

11. Find the number 675. What is 675 times 1000? Write the answer on the book.

12. Find the number 17.93. What is 17.93 times 10? Write the answer on the book.

13. Find the number 4320. What is 4320 divided by 1000? Write the answer on the book.

14. Find the number 85.4. What is 85.4 divided by 10? Write the answer on the book.

15. Find the number 8.3. What is 8.3 divided by 100? Write the answer on the book.

16. Find the number 97. Write your name on that book.

Answers

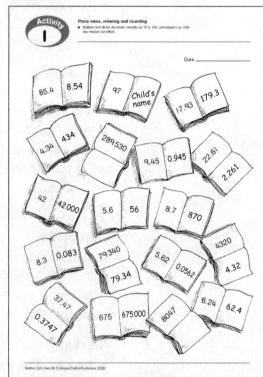

Discussion questions

↓ Choose one of the books and tell me the two numbers that are written on it.

↓ Which books did you not write on? (8047/289 530) Divide each of these numbers by 10/100. (8047: 804.7/80.47; 289 530: 28 953/2895.3)

■ What is 37.47 divided by 100? (0.3747)

■ What happens to the digits when you multiply a number by 10/100/1000? (They move one/two/three places to the left.) What happens to the digits when you divide a number by 10/100/1000? (They move one/two/three places to the right.)

↑ What is 4320 divided by 10/100/1000? (432/43.2/4.32)

↑ What is 67.21 times 10/100/1000? (672.1/6721/67 210)

Activity 1

Place value, ordering and rounding

■ Multiply and divide decimals mentally by 10 or 100, and integers by 1000, and explain the effect.

Date _____

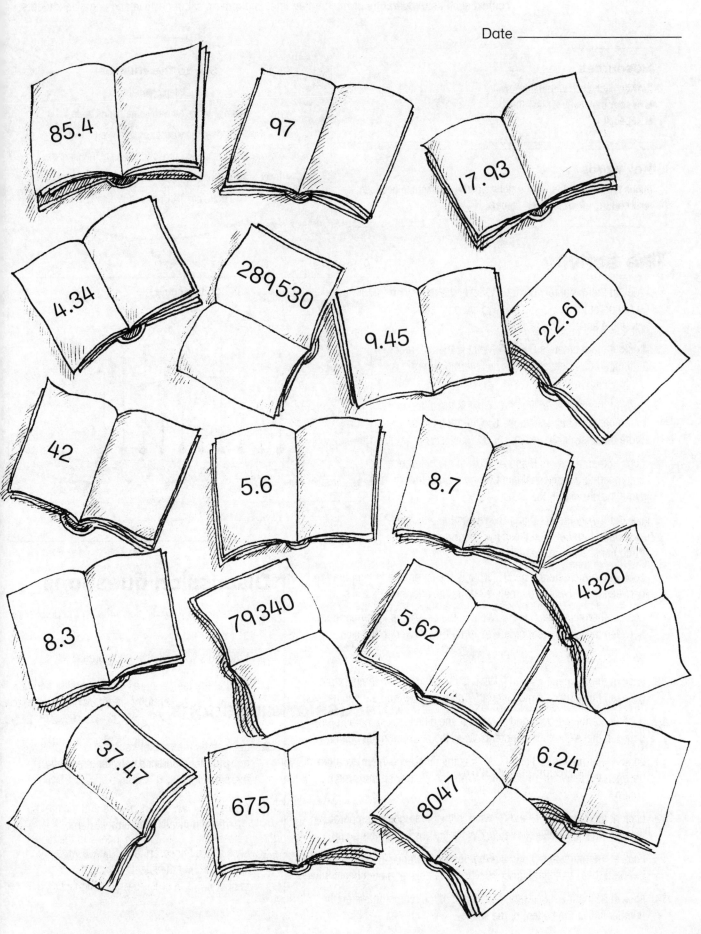

Year 6 Numbers and the number system

Place value, ordering and rounding

■ Find the difference between a positive and a negative integer, or two negative integers, in a context such as temperature or the number line, and order a set of positive and negative integers.

Resources

Provide each child with the following:
■ a copy of Activity 2 pupil sheet
■ a pencil

Key words

minus ten, minus nine, minus eight…thirty   difference between
temperature   thermometer   order

Say to the children:

Listen carefully.

I am going to tell you some things to do.

I will say them only once, so listen very carefully.

Do only the things you are told to do and nothing else.

If you make a mistake, cross it out. Do not use an eraser.

There are 14 parts to this activity.

The activity

1. Look at thermometers B and F. What is the difference in temperature between these two thermometers? Write the answer on the scarf.

2. Look at thermometers C and A. What is the difference in temperature between these two thermometers? Write the answer on the glove.

3. Look at thermometers E and G. What is the difference in temperature between these two thermometers? Write the answer on the hat.

4. Look at thermometers H and A. What is the difference in temperature between these two thermometers? Write the answer on the coat.

5. Look at thermometers B and C. What is the difference in temperature between these two thermometers? Write the answer on the umbrella.

6. Look at thermometers D and H. What is the difference in temperature between these two thermometers? Write the answer on the T-shirt.

7. Look at thermometers C and F. What is the difference in temperature between these two thermometers? Write the answer on the skis.

8. Write your name at the top of the sheet.

9. Look at thermometers G and I. What is the difference in temperature between these two thermometers? Write the answer on the sunglasses.

10. Look at thermometers B and H. What is the difference in temperature between these two thermometers? Write the answer on the boots.

11. Look at thermometers J and E. What is the difference in temperature between these two thermometers? Write the answer on the suntan cream.

12. Look at thermometers C and G. What is the difference in temperature between these two thermometers? Write the answer on the sleigh.

13. Look at thermometers D and J. What is the difference in temperature between these two thermometers? Write the answer on the beach towel.

14. Look at all the thermometers. Mark each of the temperatures on the number line at the bottom of the sheet.

Answers

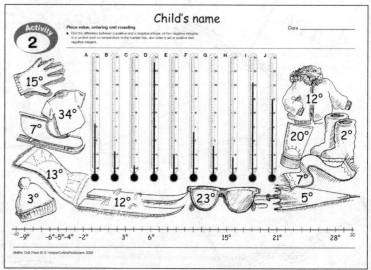

Discussion questions

↓ What temperature did you write on the umbrella? (5°)

↓ Where did you write twelve degrees? (skis)

■ Look at the temperatures on the number line. Tell me the temperatures in order coldest to hottest. (−9°, −6°, −5°, −4°, −2°, 3°, 6°, 15°, 21°, 28°)

■ Look at the thermometers C and G. What is the temperature difference between these two thermometers? (7°)

↑ Choose any two thermometers and tell me the difference between their temperatures.

↑ Look at the temperatures you have written on the objects around the sheet. Tell me these temperatures in order lowest to highest.

Date _____

Activity 2

Place value, ordering and rounding

■ Find the difference between a positive and a negative integer, or two negative integers, in a context such as temperature or the number line, and order a set of positive and negative integers.

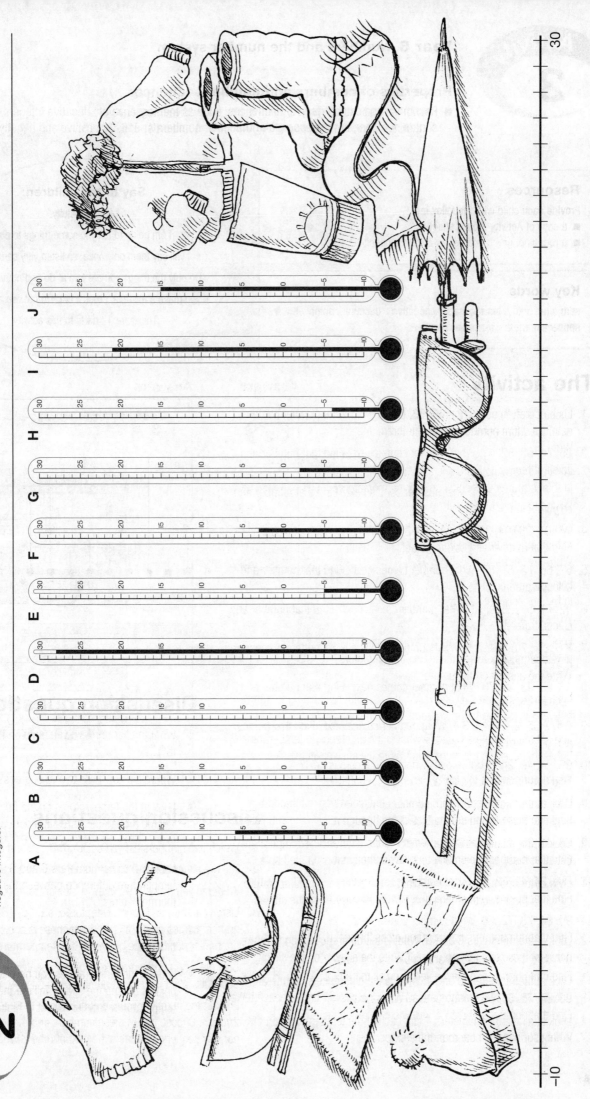

Year 6 Numbers and the number system

Properties of numbers and number sequences
- Recognise and extend number sequences, such as the sequence of square numbers, or the sequence of triangular numbers 1, 3, 6, 10, 15...

Resources

Provide each child with the following:
- a copy of Activity 3 pupil sheet
- a red, blue, green and yellow coloured pencil

Key words

zero, one, two... ten thousand   negative   decimal   point
sequence   next   triangular numbers

Say to the children:

Listen carefully.

I am going to tell you some things to do.

I will say them only once, so listen very carefully.

Do only the things you are told to do and nothing else.

If you make a mistake, cross it out. Do not use an eraser.

There are 17 parts to this activity.

The activity

1. Listen carefully as I count. 49, 56, 63, 70, 77. What number comes next? Find that number and colour it red.

2. 85, 74, 63, 52, 41. What number comes next? Find that number and colour it red.

3. 4.6, 4.7, 4.8, 4.9, 5. What number comes next? Find that number and colour it blue.

4. 34 504, 33 504, 32 504, 31 504, 30 504. What number comes next? Find that number and colour it blue.

5. 57, 65, 73, 81, 89. What number comes next? Find that number and colour it green.

6. 92, 71, 50, 29, eight. What number comes next? Find that number and colour it green.

7. 8.6, 8.1, 7.6, 7.1, 6.6. What number comes next? Find that number and colour it yellow.

8. 13, 28, 43, 58, 73. What number comes next? Find that number and colour it yellow.

9. 2.4, 2.65, 2.9, 3.15, 3.4. What number comes next? Find that number and draw a red cross through it.

10. 99, 74, 49, 24, negative one. What number comes next? Find that number and draw a red cross through it.

11. One, three, six, 10, 15. What number comes next? Find that number and draw a blue cross through it.

12. 56, 41, 26, 11, negative four. What number comes next? Find that number and draw a blue cross through it.

13. Five, 24, 43, 62, 81. What number comes next? Find that number and draw a green cross through it.

14. 90, 84, 78, 72, 66. What number comes next? Find that number and draw a green cross through it.

15. 0.7, 1.2, 1.7, 2.2, 2.7. What number comes next? Find that number and draw a yellow cross through it.

16. 93, 84, 75, 66, 57. What number comes next? Find that number and draw a yellow cross through it.

17. Write your name on the roof of the skyscraper.

Answers

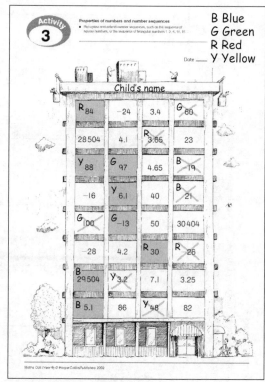

Discussion questions

↓ Which two numbers did you colour red? (30 and 84)

↓ Tell me a number you did not colour or draw a line through.

■ What did you do to −19? (drew a blue cross through it)

■ Listen carefully as I count. One, three, six, 10, 15. What number comes next? (21) What are these numbers called? (triangular numbers)

↑ Give me a number sequence involving negative numbers and decimals. What is the next number? What is the rule?

↑ Look at the numbers you did not colour or draw a cross through. Choose two of these numbers and put them into a number sequence. What is the next number? What is the rule?

Properties of numbers and number sequences

■ Recognise and extend number sequences, such as the sequence of
square numbers, or the sequence of triangular numbers 1, 3, 6, 10, 15...

Date _____

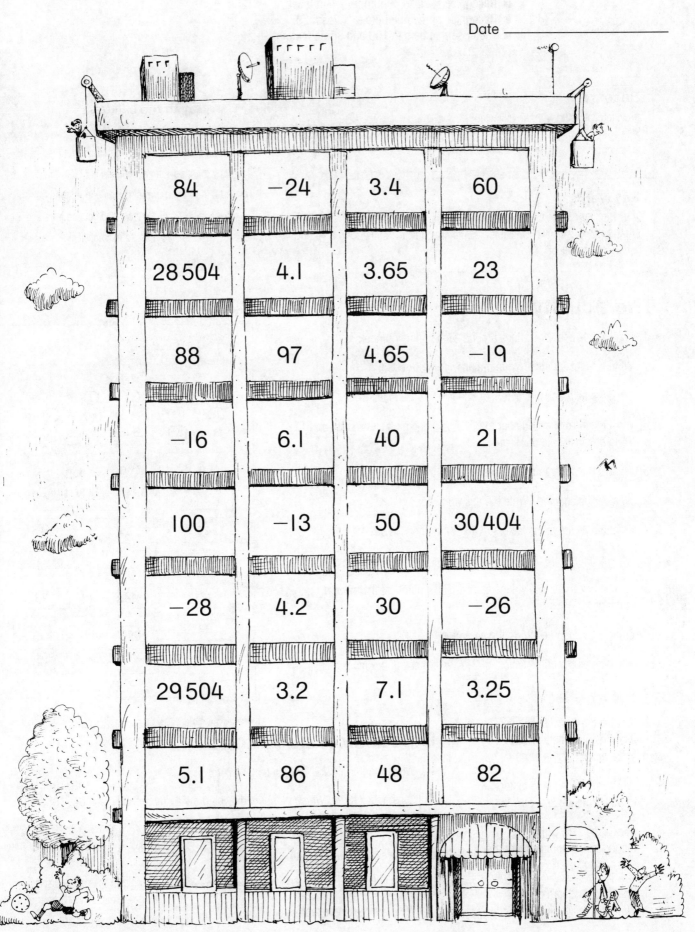

84	−24	3.4	60
28 504	4.1	3.65	23
88	97	4.65	−19
−16	6.1	40	21
100	−13	50	30 404
−28	4.2	30	−26
29 504	3.2	7.1	3.25
5.1	86	48	82

Properties of numbers and number sequences
■ Find simple common multiples.
■ Recognise squares of numbers to at least 12 × 12.
■ Recognise prime numbers to at least 20.
■ Factorise numbers to 100 into prime factors.

Resources
Provide each child with the following:
■ a copy of Activity 4 pupil sheet
■ a pencil

Key words
zero, one, two…one thousand   prime number   factor
prime factor   divisible   multiple   common multiple   squared
square of   smallest

Say to the children:
Listen carefully.
I am going to tell you some things to do.
I will say them only once, so listen very carefully.
Do only the things you are told to do and nothing else.
If you make a mistake, cross it out. Do not use an eraser.
There are 16 parts to this activity.

The activity

1. Look at box one. Draw rings around all the prime numbers.

2. What is eight squared? Write the answer in box eight.

3. What are all the prime factors of 60? Write these in box two.

4. What is the smallest number that is a common multiple of eight and 12? Write the answer in box seven.

5. What is the square of six? Write the answer in box six.

6. What is five squared? Write the answer in box five.

7. What are all the prime factors of 46? Write these in box 13.

8. What is the square of 12? Write the answer in box 12.

9. Look at box three. Draw rings around all the numbers that have a factor of 12.

10. What is 11 squared? Write the answer in box 11.

11. What are all the prime factors of 21? Write these in box nine.

12. Write your name in box 10.

13. What is the smallest number that is a common multiple of 18 and six? Write the answer in box 14.

14. What are all the prime factors of 98? Write these in box 15.

15. Look at box 16. Draw rings around all the numbers that are divisible by seven.

16. What is the square of four? Write the answer in box four.

Answers

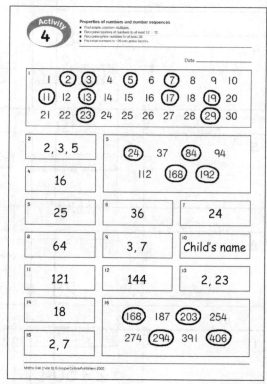

Discussion questions

↓ What number did you write in box five? (25)

↓ Look at box three. Which numbers did you draw a ring around? (24, 84, 168, 192)

■ What are all the prime numbers from one to 30? (2, 3, 5, 7, 11, 13, 17, 19, 23, 29)

■ What is 12 squared? (144)

↑ What is the smallest number that is a common multiple of eight and 12? (24)

↑ What are the prime factors of 21? (3, 7)

Properties of numbers and number sequences
- Find simple common multiples.
- Recognise squares of numbers to at least 12 × 12.
- Recognise prime numbers to at least 20.
- Factorise numbers to 100 into prime factors.

Date ___18.9.20___

1

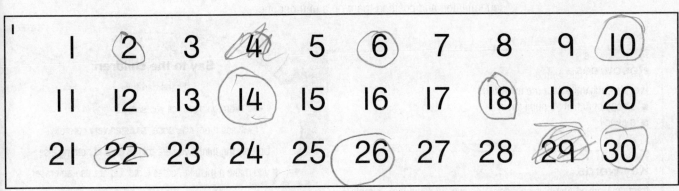

1	2	3	4	5	6	7	8	9	10
11	12	13	14	15	16	17	18	19	20
21	22	23	24	25	26	27	28	29	30

2

3

24   37   84   94

112   168   192

4

5

6

7

8

9

10   Khylie

11

12

13

14

15   27

16

168   187   203   254

274   294   391   406

Fractions, decimals and percentages

- Change a fraction such as $\frac{33}{8}$ to the equivalent mixed number $4\frac{1}{8}$, and vice versa.
- Reduce a fraction to its simplest form by cancelling common factors in the numerator and denominator.
- Order fractions such as $\frac{2}{3}$, $\frac{3}{4}$, and $\frac{5}{6}$ by converting them to fractions with a common denominator, and position them on a number line.

Resources

Provide each child with the following:
- a copy of Activity 5 pupil sheet
- a pencil

Key words

fraction   mixed number   change   equivalent   reduce   simplest

Say to the children:

Listen carefully.

I am going to tell you some things to do.

I will say them only once, so listen very carefully.

Do only the things you are told to do and nothing else.

If you make a mistake, cross it out. Do not use an eraser.

There are 5 parts to this activity.

The activity

1. Look at the fractions in Box A. Change each of these fractions to the equivalent mixed number. Write the answers in the circles.

2. Look at the mixed numbers in Box B. Change each of these mixed numbers to the equivalent fraction. Write the answers in the circles.

3. Look at the fractions in Box C. Reduce each of these fractions to its simplest form. Write the answers in the circles.

4. Look at the fractions in Box D. Mark each of these fractions on the number line.

5. Write your name on the line beside the word 'Name'.

Discussion questions

↓ Choose one of the fractions you changed to a mixed number. What is the answer?

↓ Choose a fraction from Box C and reduce it to its simplest form.

■ What is eight and four sevenths as a fraction? ($\frac{60}{7}$)

■ How do you change a fraction to a mixed number? How do you change a mixed number to a fraction? How do you reduce a fraction to its simplest form?

↑ Tell me a mixed number. What is this as a fraction?

↑ Look at the number line. Tell me the fractions in order, smallest to largest. ($\frac{1}{6}$, $\frac{1}{4}$, $\frac{1}{3}$, $\frac{1}{2}$, $\frac{2}{3}$, $\frac{3}{4}$, $\frac{5}{6}$)

Answers

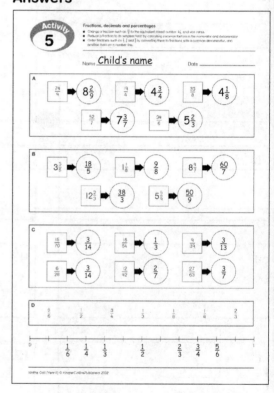

Activity 5

Fractions, decimals and percentages

- Change a fraction such as $\frac{33}{8}$ to the equivalent mixed number $4\frac{1}{8}$, and vice versa.
- Reduce a fraction to its simplest form by cancelling common factors in the numerator and denominator.
- Order fractions such as $\frac{2}{3}$, $\frac{3}{4}$ and $\frac{5}{6}$ by converting them to fractions with a common denominator, and position them on a number line.

Name _____   Date _____

A

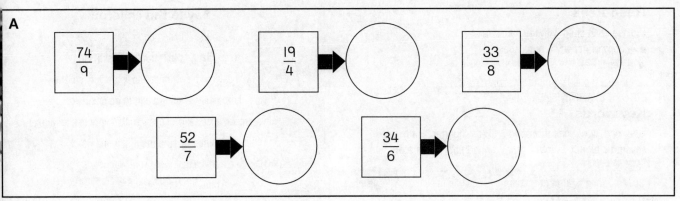

B

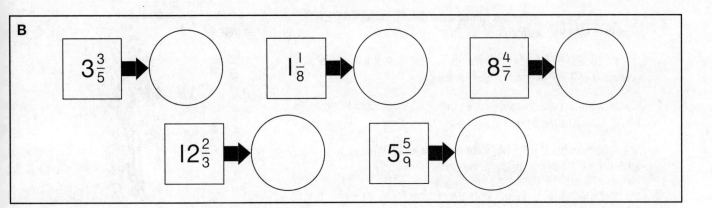

C

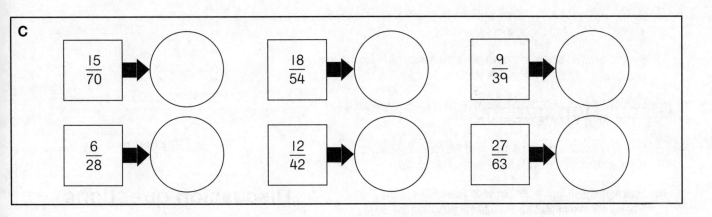

D

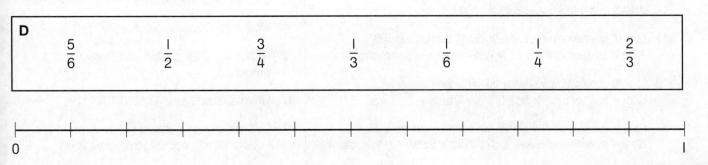

Fractions, decimals and percentages

■ Use a fraction as an 'operator' to find fractions, including tenths and hundredths, of numbers or quantities (e.g. $\frac{5}{8}$ of 32, $\frac{7}{10}$ of 40, $\frac{9}{100}$ of 400 centimetres).

Resources

Provide each child with the following:
■ a copy of Activity 6 pupil sheet
■ a pencil

Key words

zero, one, two…one thousand third quarter fifth sixth
seventh eighth ninth tenth hundredth operator

Say to the children:

Listen carefully.

I am going to tell you some things to do.

I will say them only once, so listen very carefully.

Do only the things you are told to do and nothing else.

If you make a mistake, cross it out. Do not use an eraser.

There are 15 parts to this activity.

The activity

1. Look at question one. In the box write the number 70. What is three tenths of 70? Write the answer in the circle.

2. Look at question two. In the box write the number 400. What is eight hundredths of 400? Write the answer in the circle.

3. Look at question three. In the box write the number 75. What is three fifths of 75? Write the answer in the circle.

4. Look at question four. In the box write the number 32. What is five eighths of 32? Write the answer in the circle.

5. Look at question five. In the box write the number 60. What is nine tenths of 60? Write the answer in the circle.

6. Look at question six. In the box write the number 64. What is seven eighths of 64? Write the answer in the circle.

7. Look at question seven. In the box write the number 84. What is four sevenths of 84? Write the answer in the circle.

8. Look at question eight. In the box write the number 63. What is five ninths of 63? Write the answer in the circle.

9. Look at question nine. In the box write the number 32. What is three quarters of 32? Write the answer in the circle.

10. Look at question ten. In the box write the number 300. What is seven tenths of 300? Write the answer in the circle.

11. Write your name at the bottom of the sheet.

12. Look at question eleven. In the box write the number 700. What is six hundredths of 700? Write the answer in the circle.

13. Look at question twelve. In the box write the number 56. What is two sevenths of 56? Write the answer in the circle.

14. Look at question thirteen. In the box write the number 300. What is three hundredths of 300? Write the answer in the circle.

15. Look at question fourteen. In the box write the number 180. What is five sixths of 180? Write the answer in the circle.

Answers

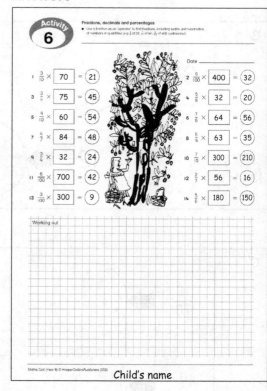

Discussion questions

↓ Choose one of the questions and tell me the answer.

↓ What is the answer to question five? (54)

■ Choose one of the questions and explain how you worked it out.

■ Which question has an answer of 16? (12)

↑ Did you make any mistakes? If so, where did you make an error? What will you do next time?

↑ When might you need to use fractions as an 'operator' to find fractions of numbers? (e.g. measures, sales)

Fractions, decimals and percentages

■ Use a fraction as an 'operator' to find fractions, including tenths and hundredths, of numbers or quantities (e.g. $\frac{5}{8}$ of 32, $\frac{7}{10}$ of 40, $\frac{9}{100}$ of 400 centimetres).

Date _____

1 $\frac{3}{10} \times$ ☐ = ◯

2 $\frac{8}{100} \times$ ☐ = ◯

3 $\frac{3}{5} \times$ ☐ = ◯

4 $\frac{5}{8} \times$ ☐ = ◯

5 $\frac{9}{10} \times$ ☐ = ◯

6 $\frac{7}{8} \times$ ☐ = ◯

7 $\frac{4}{7} \times$ ☐ = ◯

8 $\frac{5}{9} \times$ ☐ = ◯

9 $\frac{3}{4} \times$ ☐ = ◯

10 $\frac{7}{10} \times$ ☐ = ◯

11 $\frac{6}{100} \times$ ☐ = ◯

12 $\frac{2}{7} \times$ ☐ = ◯

13 $\frac{3}{100} \times$ ☐ = ◯

14 $\frac{5}{6} \times$ ☐ = ◯

Working out

Fractions, decimals and percentages

- Know what each digit represents in a number with up to three decimal places.
- Give a decimal fraction lying between two others (e.g. between 3.4 and 3.5).
- Order a mixed set of numbers or measurements with up to three decimal places.
- Round a number with two decimal places to the nearest tenth or to the nearest whole number.

Resources

Provide each child with the following:
- a copy of Activity 7 pupil sheet
- a pencil

Key words

tenth hundredth thousandth order round rounded to
decimal decimal fraction whole number point worth
represent equivalent nearest smallest shortest lightest
largest longest heaviest

Say to the children:

Listen carefully.

I am going to tell you some things to do.

I will say them only once, so listen very carefully.

Do only the things you are told to do and nothing else.

If you make a mistake, cross it out. Do not use an eraser.

There are 15 parts to this activity.

The activity

1. What does the digit seven in 3.297 represent? Write the answer on flag five.

2. What is the two worth in the number 9.328? Write the answer on flag nine.

3. Look at the measurements at the top of the sheet. Put these distances in order, shortest first. Write the answer on golf club one.

4. What is the decimal fraction equivalent to four tenths, eight hundredths and two thousandths? Write the answer on flag three.

5. What is the decimal fraction equivalent to five and seven thousandths? Write the answer on flag number six.

6. What is the decimal fraction equivalent to fourteen and thirty-six thousandths? Write the answer on flag number two.

7. Write your name on flag one.

8. What is 27.63 rounded to the nearest whole number? Write the answer on flag seven.

9. Look at the decimals at the top of the sheet. Put these decimals in order, smallest first. Write the answer on golf club two.

10. What is 6.34 rounded to the nearest tenth? Write the answer on flag eight.

11. Look at the weights at the top of the sheet. Put these weights in order, lightest first. Write the answer on golf club three.

12. What is 3.87 rounded to one decimal place? Write the answer on flag four.

13. Look at the first set of golf balls. On the middle ball write a number that lies between 3.6 and 3.7.

14. Look at the second set of golf balls. On the middle ball write a number that lies between 2.35 and 2.36.

15. Look at the third set of golf balls. On the middle ball write a number that lies between 9.4 and 9.45.

Answers

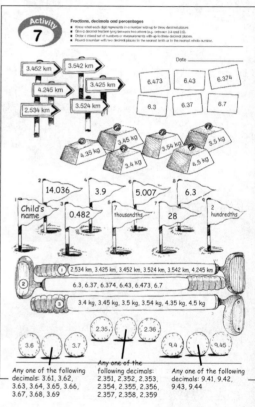

Discussion questions

↓ What number did you write on flag seven? (28)

↓ What is the decimal fraction equivalent to fourteen and thirty-six thousandths? (14.036)

■ Look at the decimals at the top of the sheet. Tell me these decimals in order, smallest first. (6.3, 6.37, 6.374, 6.43, 6.473, 6.7)

■ Look at the first set of golf balls. What number did you write on the middle golf ball? What other numbers could you have written? (Any one of the following decimals: 3.61, 3.62, 3.63, 3.64, 3.65, 3.66, 3.67, 3.68, 3.69)

↑ What is 3.452 rounded to the nearest whole number/tenth/hundredth? (3/3.5/3.45)

↑ Choose a decimal on the sheet and round it to the nearest whole number/tenth/hundredth.

Fractions, decimals and percentages

- Know what each digit represents in a number with up to three decimal places.
- Give a decimal fraction lying between two others (e.g. between 3.4 and 3.5).
- Order a mixed set of numbers or measurements with up to three decimal places.
- Round a number with two decimal places to the nearest tenth or to the nearest whole number.

Date _____

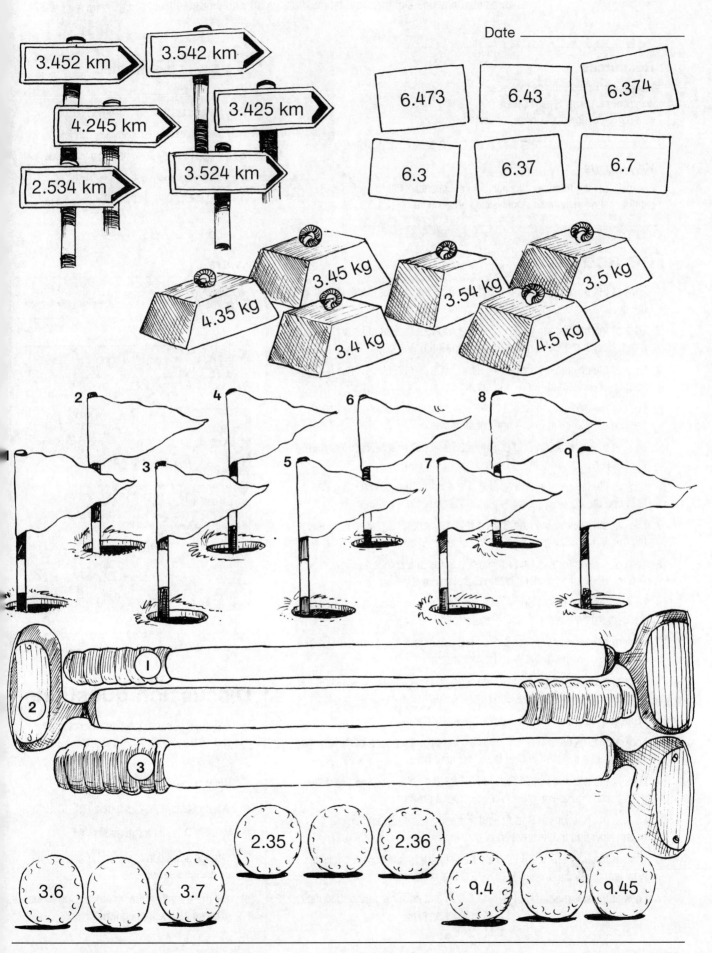

Fractions, decimals and percentages

- Recognise the equivalence between the decimal and fraction forms of one half, one quarter, three quarters, one eighth… and tenths, hundredths and thousandths (e.g. $\frac{700}{1000} = \frac{70}{100} = \frac{7}{10} = 0.7$).

Resources

Provide each child with the following:
- a copy of Activity 8 pupil sheet
- a red, blue, green and yellow coloured pencil

Key words

decimal point fraction one half third quarter fifth
eighth tenth hundredth equivalent thousandth

Say to the children:

Listen carefully.

I am going to tell you some things to do.

I will say them only once, so listen very carefully.

Do only the things you are told to do and nothing else.

If you make a mistake, cross it out. Do not use an eraser.

There are 17 parts to this activity.

The activity

1. Look at the fractions in Grid A. Find one third and colour it red. Now find the decimal equivalent in Grid B and colour it red.

2. Look at the fractions in Grid A. Find five and four thousandths and colour it red. Now find the decimal equivalent in Grid B and colour it red.

3. Look at the decimals in Grid B. Find 0.03 and colour it blue. Now find the fraction equivalent in Grid A and colour it blue.

4. Look at the decimals in Grid B. Find 5.2 and colour it blue. Now find the fraction equivalent in Grid A and colour it blue.

5. Look at the decimals in Grid B. Find 5.35 and colour it green. Now find the fraction equivalent in Grid A and colour it green.

6. Look at the fractions in Grid A. Find one hundredth and colour it green. Now find the decimal equivalent in Grid B and colour it green.

7. Look at the decimals in Grid B. Find 0.25 and colour it yellow. Now find the fraction equivalent in Grid A and colour it yellow.

8. Look at the fractions in Grid A. Find two thirds and colour it yellow. Now find the decimal equivalent in Grid B and colour it yellow.

9. Look at the fractions in Grid A. Find one eighth and colour it red. Now find the decimal equivalent in Grid B and colour it red.

10. Look at the decimals in Grid B. Find 0.2 and colour it red. Now find the fraction equivalent in Grid A and colour it red.

11. Look at the decimals in Grid B. Find 5.04 and colour it blue. Now find the fraction equivalent in Grid A and colour it blue.

12. Write your name on the line beside the word 'Name'.

13. Look at the fractions in Grid A. Find one tenth and colour it blue. Now find the decimal equivalent in Grid B and colour it blue.

14. Look at the decimals in Grid B. Find 0.008 and colour it green. Now find the fraction equivalent in Grid A and colour it green.

15. Look at the fractions in Grid A. Find five and four tenths and colour it green. Now find the decimal equivalent in Grid B and colour it green.

16. Look at the fractions in Grid A. Find three quarters and colour it yellow. Now find the decimal equivalent in Grid B and colour it yellow.

17. Look at the decimals in Grid B. Find 5.035 and colour it yellow. Now find the fraction equivalent in Grid A and colour it yellow.

Answers

B Blue
G Green
R Red
Y Yellow

Name __Child's name__ Date ___

Grid A

R	Y	G	B
$5\frac{4}{1000}$	$\frac{3}{4}$	$\frac{1}{100}$	$5\frac{1}{5}$
B $\frac{1}{10}$	**G** $5\frac{35}{100}$	**Y** $\frac{1}{4}$	**G** $5\frac{4}{10}$
R $\frac{1}{3}$	**R** $\frac{1}{8}$	**G** $\frac{8}{1000}$	**Y** $5\frac{35}{1000}$
B $\frac{3}{100}$	**R** $\frac{1}{5}$	**B** $5\frac{4}{100}$	**Y** $\frac{2}{3}$

Grid B

Y	G	G	Y
0.75	0.008	5.4	0.666
B 0.03	**B** 5.2	**Y** 5.035	**R** 0.2
G 5.35	**R** 0.125	**R** 0.333	**B** 5.04
G 0.01	**B** 0.1	**Y** 0.25	**R** 5.004

Discussion questions

↓ Tell me a decimal/fraction you coloured red. (0.125, 0.2, 0.333, 5.004/ $\frac{1}{8}, \frac{1}{3}, \frac{1}{5}, 5\frac{4}{1000}$)

↓ What colour is one tenth? (blue)

■ What is one eighth as a decimal? (0.125)

■ What is 0.25 as a fraction? ($\frac{1}{4}$)

↑ Choose a fraction from Grid A and tell me its decimal equivalent.

↑ Tell me a fraction that is not on Grid A and give me its decimal equivalent.

Activity 8

Fractions, decimals and percentages

■ Recognise the equivalence between the decimal and fraction forms
of one half, one quarter, three quarters, one eighth… and tenths,
hundredths and thousandths (e.g. $\frac{700}{1000} = \frac{70}{100} = \frac{7}{10} = 0.7$).

Name ___Terry___   Date ___13 DEC___

Grid A

$5\frac{4}{1000}$	1. $\frac{3}{4}$	3. $\frac{1}{100}$	11. $5\frac{1}{5}$ $\frac{26}{5}$
2. $\frac{1}{10}$	$5\frac{35}{100}$	4. $\frac{1}{4}$	$5\frac{4}{10}$
7. $\frac{1}{3}$	6. $\frac{1}{8}$	5. $\frac{8}{1000}$	$5\frac{35}{1000}$
8. $\frac{3}{100}$	9. $\frac{1}{5}$	$5\frac{4}{100}$	10. $\frac{2}{3}$

Grid B

1. 0.75	3. 0.008	5.4	10. 0.666
8. 0.03	11. 5.2	5.035	9. 0.2
5.35	6. 0.125	7. 0.333	5.04
3. 0.01	0.1	2. 4. 0.25	5.004

Year 6 Numbers and the number system

Fractions, decimals and percentages

- Express simple fractions such as one half, one quarter, three quarters, one third, two thirds…, and tenths and hundredths, as percentages (e.g. know that $\frac{1}{3} = 33\frac{1}{3}\%$).
- Find simple percentages of small whole-number quantities (e.g. find 10% of £500, then 20%, 40% and 80% by doubling).

Resources

Provide each child with the following:
- a copy of Activity 9 pupil sheet
- a red, blue, green and yellow coloured pencil
- a calculator (optional)

Key words

one half   third   one quarter   three quarters   tenth   hundredth
fraction   percentage   equivalent

Say to the children:

Listen carefully.

I am going to tell you some things to do.

I will say them only once, so listen very carefully.

Do only the things you are told to do and nothing else.

If you make a mistake, cross it out. Do not use an eraser.

There are 16 parts to this activity.

The activity

1. Look at the fractions in Grid A. Find three quarters and colour it red. Now find the percentage equivalent in Grid B and colour it red.

2. Look at the fractions in Grid A. Find one half and colour it blue. Now find the percentage equivalent in Grid B and colour it blue.

3. Look at the percentages in Grid B. Find 10 per cent and colour it green. Now find the fraction equivalent in Grid A and colour it green.

4. Look at the percentages in Grid B. Find 25 per cent and colour it yellow. Now find the fraction equivalent in Grid A and colour it yellow.

5. Look at the fractions in Grid A. Find seven tenths and colour it red. Now find the percentage equivalent in Grid B and colour it red.

6. Look at the percentages in Grid B. Find one per cent and colour it blue. Now find the fraction equivalent in Grid A and colour it blue.

7. Look at the fractions in Grid A. Find one third and colour it green. Now find the percentage equivalent in Grid B and colour it green.

8. Look at the percentages in Grid B. Find 66.6 per cent and colour it yellow. Now find the fraction equivalent in Grid A and colour it yellow.

9. What is 50 per cent of 96? Write the answer on balloon one.

10. What is 10 per cent of 300? Write the answer on balloon two.

11. What is 75 per cent of 56? Write the answer on balloon three.

12. What is 40 per cent of 600? Write the answer on balloon four.

13. Write your name on balloon five.

14. What is 25 per cent of 112? Write the answer on balloon six.

15. What is 20 per cent of 250? Write the answer on balloon seven.

16. What is 70 per cent of 400? Write the answer on balloon eight.

Answers

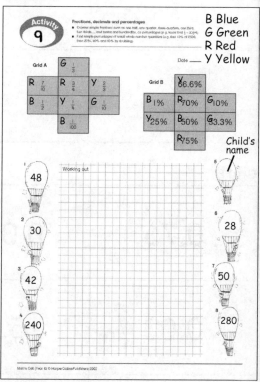

Discussion questions

↓ What fractions and percentages did you colour blue? ($\frac{1}{2}$, $\frac{1}{100}$, 50%, 1%)

↓ What is one quarter as a percentage? (25%)

■ What is 40 per cent of 600? (240)

■ Choose a percentage calculation you did and explain how you worked it out. Did anyone use a different method?

↑ What other percentages do you know? Choose one and use it to work out the percentage of a whole number.

↑ If VAT is $17\frac{1}{2}$ per cent of the price of an item, how would you work that out?

Fractions, decimals and percentages

- Express simple fractions such as one half, one quarter, three quarters, one third, two thirds…, and tenths and hundredths, as percentages (e.g. know that $\frac{1}{3} = 33\frac{1}{3}\%$).
- Find simple percentages of small whole-number quantities (e.g. find 10% of £500, then 20%, 40% and 80% by doubling).

Date _____

Grid A

	$\frac{1}{3}$	
$\frac{7}{10}$	$\frac{3}{4}$	$\frac{2}{3}$
$\frac{1}{2}$	$\frac{1}{4}$	$\frac{1}{10}$
	$\frac{1}{100}$	

Grid B

	66.6%	
1%	70%	10%
25%	50%	33.3%
	75%	

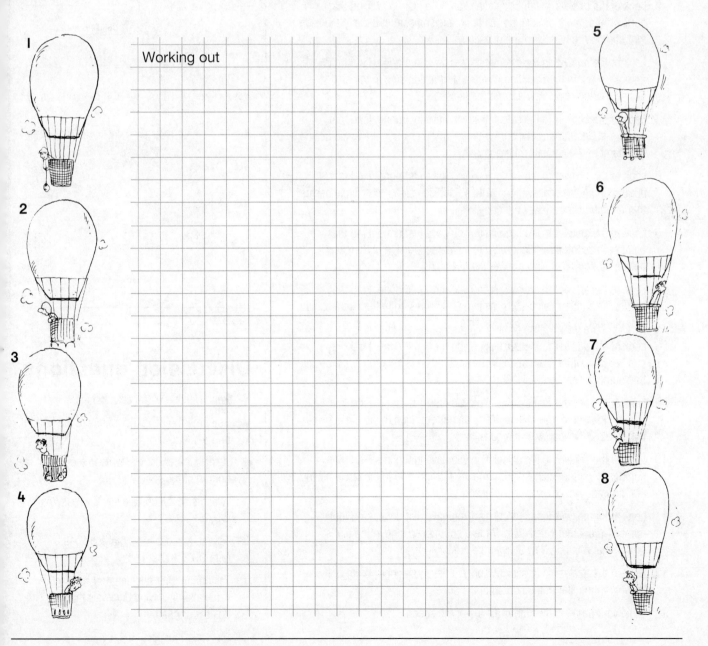

Working out

1
2
3
4
5
6
7
8

Year 6 Calculations

Addition and subtraction

■ Use known number facts and place value to consolidate mental addition/subtraction (e.g. 470 + 330, 810 − 380, 7.4 + 9.8, 9.2 − 8.6).

Resources

Provide each child with the following:
■ a copy of Activity 10 pupil sheet
■ a pencil

Key words

zero, one, two…ten   addition   subtraction   decimal   point

Say to the children:

Listen carefully.

I am going to tell you some things to do.

I will say them only once, so listen very carefully.

Do only the things you are told to do and nothing else.

If you make a mistake, cross it out. Do not use an eraser.

There are 13 parts to this activity.

The activity

1. Find 0.9. Write a subtraction sign in the circle beside that number. Now answer the question.

2. Look at the answer to the calculation you have just done. Find that number in another calculation. Write an addition sign in the circle beside that number. Now answer the question.

3. Look at the answer to the calculation you have just done. Find that number in another calculation. Write a subtraction sign in the circle beside that number. Now answer the question.

4. Look at the answer to the calculation you have just done. Find that number in another calculation. Write an addition sign in the circle beside that number. Now answer the question.

5. Look at the answer to the calculation you have just done. Find that number in another calculation. Write an addition sign in the circle beside that number. Now answer the question.

6. Look at the answer to the calculation you have just done. Find that number in another calculation. Write a subtraction sign in the circle beside that number. Now answer the question.

7. Look at the answer to the calculation you have just done. Find that number in another calculation. Write an addition sign in the circle beside that number. Now answer the question.

8. Look at the answer to the calculation you have just done. Find that number in another calculation. Write an addition sign in the circle beside that number. Now answer the question.

9. Look at the answer to the calculation you have just done. Find that number in another calculation. Write an addition sign in the circle beside that number. Now answer the question.

10. Look at the answer to the calculation you have just done. Find that number in another calculation. Write an addition sign in the circle beside that number. Now answer the question.

11. Look at the answer to the calculation you have just done. Find that number in another calculation. Write a subtraction sign in the circle beside that number. Now answer the question.

12. Look at the answer to the calculation you have just done. Write that number in the star at the bottom of the sheet.

13. Write your name in the star at the top of the sheet.

Answers

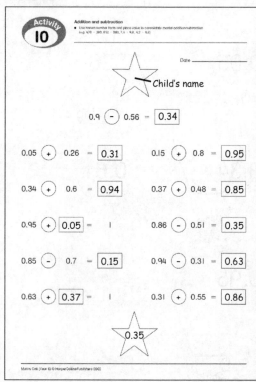

Discussion questions

↓ Read me one of the calculations.

↓ Read me the two calculations at the bottom of the sheet.

■ What number did you write in the star at the bottom of the sheet? (0.35)

■ Which calculations did you find easy/hard? Why?

↑ Tell me two decimals that total one. (e.g. 0.73 + 0.27)

↑ Tell me another addition and subtraction calculation involving decimals that you can do in your head.

Addition and subtraction

■ Use known number facts and place value to consolidate mental addition/subtraction
(e.g. 470 + 380, 810 − 380, 7.4 + 9.8, 9.2 − 8.6)

Date _____

$$0.9 \bigcirc 0.56 = \boxed{}$$

$$0.05 \bigcirc 0.26 = \boxed{} \qquad 0.15 \bigcirc 0.8 = \boxed{}$$

$$0.34 \bigcirc 0.6 = \boxed{} \qquad 0.37 \bigcirc 0.48 = \boxed{}$$

$$0.95 \bigcirc \boxed{} = 1 \qquad 0.86 \bigcirc 0.51 = \boxed{}$$

$$0.85 \bigcirc 0.7 = \boxed{} \qquad 0.94 \bigcirc 0.31 = \boxed{}$$

$$0.63 \bigcirc \boxed{} = 1 \qquad 0.31 \bigcirc 0.55 = \boxed{}$$

Year 6 Calculations

Addition and subtraction

- Use informal pencil and paper methods to support, record or explain additions and subtractions.
- Extend written methods to column addition and subtraction of numbers involving decimals.

Resources

Provide each child with the following:
- a copy of Activity 11 pupil sheet
- a pencil
- a calculator (optional)

Key words

zero, one, two…one thousand   decimal   point   tenth
hundredth   add   total   sum   difference   subtract

Say to the children:

Listen carefully.

I am going to tell you some things to do.

I will say them only once, so listen very carefully.

Do only the things you are told to do and nothing else.

If you make a mistake, cross it out. Do not use an eraser.

There are 7 parts to this activity.

The activity

1. Look at the numbers in the columns. Draw a ring around the numbers 234.9 and 4.93. Add these two numbers together and write the answer in box one.

2. Look at the numbers in the columns. Draw a ring around the numbers 305.9 and 7.32. Find the difference between these two numbers and write the answer in box two.

3. Look at the numbers in the columns. Draw a ring around the numbers 15.6 and 482.68. Subtract the smaller number from the larger number and write the answer in box three.

4. Look at the numbers in the columns. Draw a ring around the numbers 43.1 and 12.74. Find the total of these two numbers and write the answer in box four.

5. Look at the numbers in the columns. Draw a ring around the numbers 85.3 and 8.63. Find the difference between these two numbers and write the answer in box five.

6. Look at the numbers in the columns. Draw a ring around the numbers 534.89 and 182.3. Find the sum of these two numbers and write the answer in box six.

7. Write your name at the top of the sheet.

Answers

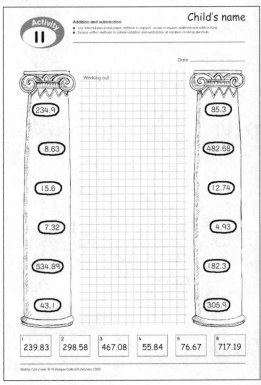

Discussion questions

↓ Tell me one of the numbers you wrote in the boxes.

↓ Which calculations did you find easy/hard? Why?

■ Choose one of the calculations you did and explain to us how you worked it out. Did anyone work it out using a different method?

■ What number did you write in box four? (55.84)

↑ What is the total of these three numbers: 8.63, 15.6 and 43.1? (67.33)

↑ Look at the numbers you have written in the boxes. Choose two of these numbers and tell me the sum of/difference between these two numbers.

Addition and subtraction

■ Use informal pencil and paper methods to support, record or explain additions and subtractions.
■ Extend written methods to column addition and subtraction of numbers involving decimals.

Date _____

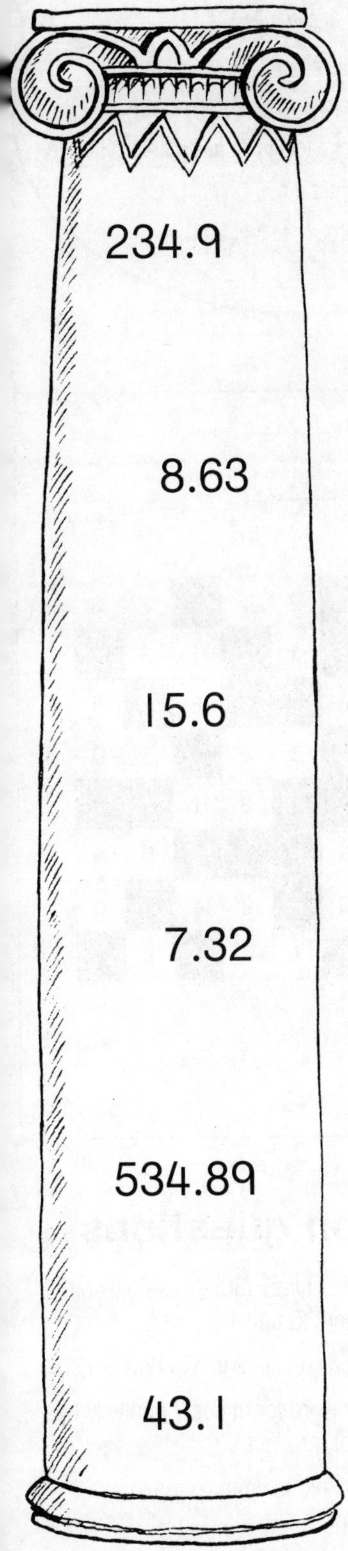

Working out

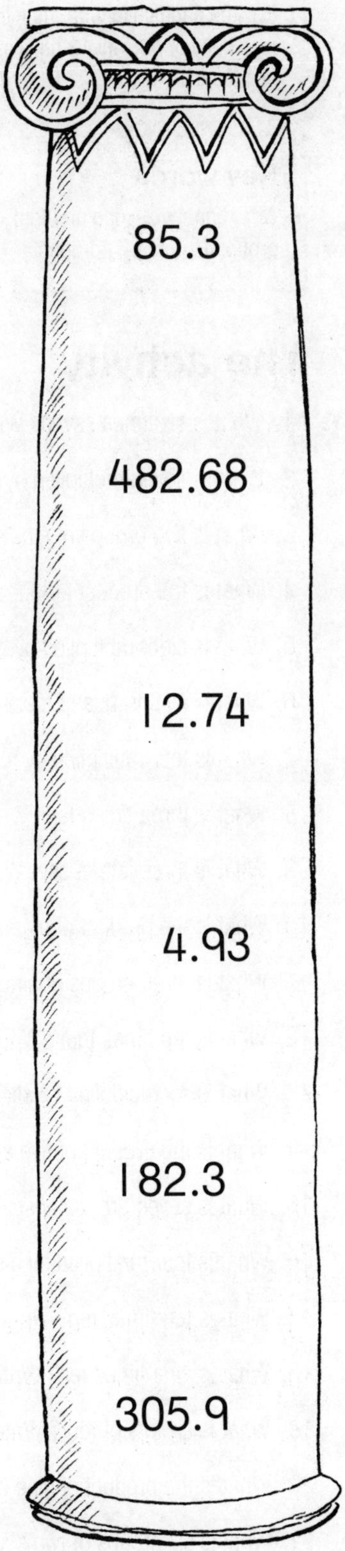

234.9

8.63

15.6

7.32

534.89

43.1

85.3

482.68

12.74

4.93

182.3

305.9

1	2	3	4	5	6

Activity 12

Multiplication

■ Consolidate knowing by heart multiplication facts up to 10 × 10.

Resources

Provide each child with the following:
■ a copy of Activity 12 pupil sheet
■ a pencil

Key words

zero, one, two…one hundred   times   multiply   multiplied by
group of   lots of   product

Say to the children:

Listen carefully.

I am going to tell you some things to do.

I will say them only once, so listen very carefully.

Do only the things you are told to do and nothing else.

If you make a mistake, cross it out. Do not use an eraser.

There are 24 parts to this activity.

The activity

1. What is six times seven? Write the answer in one across.

2. What is seven multiplied by five? Write the answer in five down.

3. What is two groups of nine? Write the answer in four across.

4. What is the product of four and eight? Write the answer in eight across.

5. What is eight multiplied by six? Write the answer in one down.

6. What is five groups of four? Write the answer in three across.

7. What is four multiplied by four? Write the answer in four down.

8. What is three times ten? Write the answer in nine across.

9. What is three lots of seven? Write the answer in two down.

10. What is the product of nine and six? Write the answer in twelve across.

11. What is three groups of nine? Write the answer in two across.

12. What is ten times four? Write the answer in thirteen down.

13. What is six multiplied by six? Write the answer in five across.

14. What is the product of five and nine? Write the answer in seven across.

15. What is seven groups of seven? Write the answer in seven down.

16. What is four multiplied by nine? Write the answer in eleven across.

17. What is ten times ten? Write the answer in fourteen across.

18. What is nine times ten? Write the answer in six down.

19. What is six lots of four? Write the answer in fifteen across.

20. What is the product of nine and nine? Write the answer in ten across.

21. What is six groups of two? Write the answer in fourteen down.

22. What is seven times two? Write the answer in sixteen across.

23. What is three multiplied by three? Write the answer in seventeen across.

24. Write your name below the date.

Answers

Discussion questions

↓ What is four times nine? (36) Where did you write this number? (5 and 11 across)

↓ What number did you write in two down? (21)

■ What is another word for 'times'? (multiply by, lots of, groups of, product)

■ Where were you told to write your name? (below the date)

↑ Look at 15 across. What are all the pairs of factors for 24? (1 and 24, 2 and 12, 3 and 8, 4 and 6)

↑ Which multiplication tables are you confident in? Which tables do you need to work on?

Multiplication

■ Consolidate knowing by heart multiplication facts up to 10 × 10.

Name _____   Date _____

Year 6 Calculations

Multiplication

- Use informal pencil and paper methods to support, record or explain multiplications.
- Extend written methods to multiplication of ThHTU × U (short multiplication).

Resources

Provide each child with the following:
- a copy of Activity 13 pupil sheet
- a pencil
- a calculator (optional)

Key words

zero, one, two…one hundred thousand   answer   times   multiply
multiplied by   group of   lots of   product

Say to the children:

Listen carefully.

I am going to tell you some things to do.

I will say them only once, so listen very carefully.

Do only the things you are told to do and nothing else.

If you make a mistake, cross it out. Do not use an eraser.

There are 13 parts to this activity.

The activity

1. Look at question one. Write the number six in the box and work out the answer.

2. Now look at the cross-number puzzle at the bottom of the sheet. Write the answer to question one in one down.

3. Look at question two. Write the number nine in the box and work out the answer.

4. Now look at the cross-number puzzle. Write the answer to question two in one across.

5. Look at question three. Write the number four in the box and work out the answer.

6. Now look at the cross-number puzzle. Write the answer to question three in two down.

7. Look at question four. Write the number five in the box and work out the answer.

8. Now look at the cross-number puzzle. Write the answer to question four in three down.

9. Look at question five. Write the number seven in the box and work out the answer.

10. Now look at the cross-number puzzle. Write the answer to question five in four across.

11. Look at question six. Write the number eight in the box and work out the answer.

12. Now look at the cross-number puzzle. Write the answer to question six in five across.

13. Write your name under the line beside the word 'Name'.

Answers

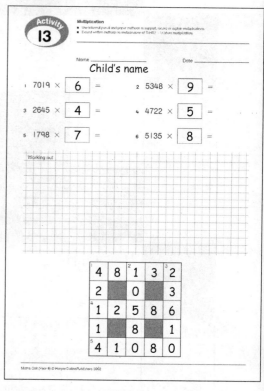

Discussion questions

↓ Look at the cross-number puzzle. Tell me one of the numbers you wrote down.

↓ Look at your working out. Choose a calculation and tell me how you worked it out.

■ What is the answer to question three? (10 580)

■ Which calculation has the answer 41 080? (6)

↑ Did anyone work out any of these calculations in their head? How did you do it?

↑ Which method did you use to work out these answers? Did anyone use a different method?

Multiplication

■ Use informal pencil and paper methods to support, record or explain multiplications.
■ Extend written methods to multiplication of ThHTU × U (short multiplication).

Name _____ Date _____

1 7019 × [   ] =   2 5348 × [   ] =

3 2645 × [   ] =   4 4722 × [   ] =

5 1798 × [   ] =   6 5135 × [   ] =

Working out

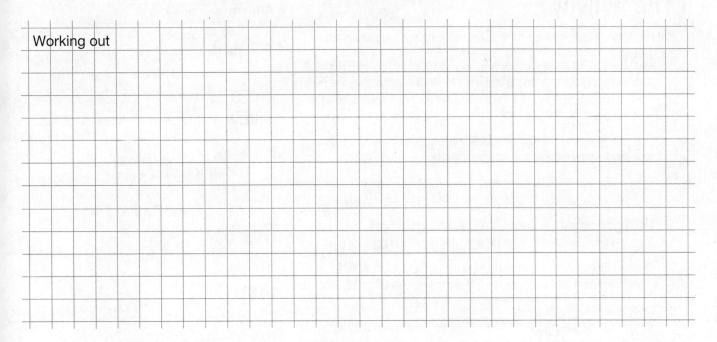

Year 6 Calculations

Multiplication

- Use informal pencil and paper methods to support, record or explain multiplications.
- Extend written methods to short multiplication of numbers involving decimals.

Resources

Provide each child with the following:
- a copy of Activity 14 pupil sheet
- a pencil
- a calculator (optional)

You will also need a 0 – 9 die

Key words

zero, one, two…one thousand   decimal   point   times   product
multiplied by

Say to the children:

Listen carefully.

I am going to tell you some things to do.

I will say them only once, so listen very carefully.

Do only the things you are told to do and nothing else.

If you make a mistake, cross it out. Do not use an eraser.

There are 7 parts to this activity.

The activity

Note: Italicised instructions are for the teacher and are not to be read out to the children.

1. Look at the numbers at the top of the sheet. Draw a ring around the number 5.87. What is 5.87 times *(roll the die and call out the number)*? Write the answer on star number one.

2. Draw a ring around the number 43.06. What is the product of 43.06 and *(roll the die and call out the number)*? Write the answer on star number two.

3. Draw a ring around the number 8.82. What is 8.82 multiplied by *(roll the die and call out the number)*? Write the answer on star number three.

4. Draw a ring around the number 72.73. What is 72.73 times *(roll the die and call out the number)*? Write the answer on star number four.

5. Draw a ring around the number 692.5. What is the product of 692.5 and *(roll the die and call out the number)*? Write the answer on star number five.

6. Draw a ring around the number 29.41. What is 29.41 multiplied by *(roll the die and call out the number)*? Write the answer on star number six.

7. Write your name on the line near the word 'Name'.

Answers

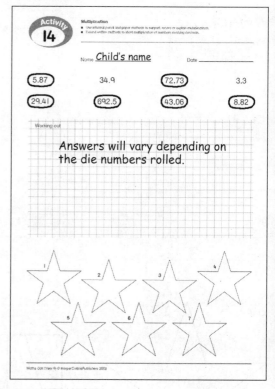

Discussion questions

↓ Tell me a number you wrote on one of the stars.

↓ What number did you write on star number three?

■ Choose a calculation you did and explain how you worked it out. Did anyone use a different method?

■ What did you find easy/difficult about this activity?

↑ Look at the number 34.9. Approximately what is 34.9 multiplied by six? (210)

↑ Did you work out the answers to any of these calculations in your heads? How did you do it? Did anyone work it out a different way?

Activity 14

Multiplication

■ Use informal pencil and paper methods to support, record or explain multiplications.
■ Extend written methods to short multiplication of numbers involving decimals.

Name _____   Date _____

5.87	34.9	72.73	3.3
29.41	692.5	43.06	8.82

Working out

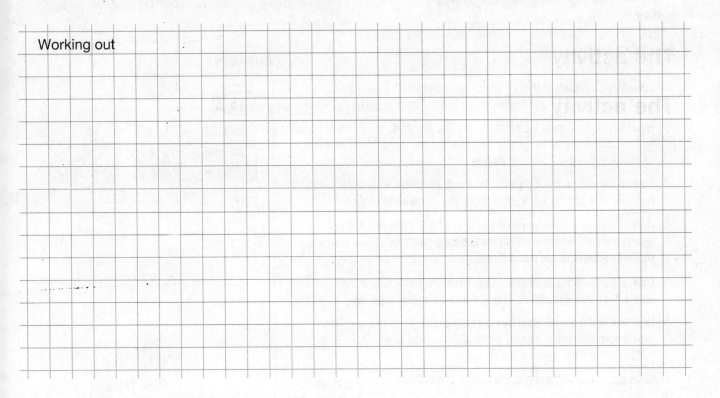

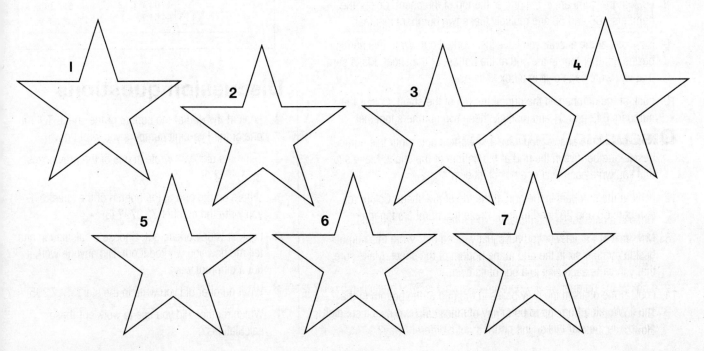

Multiplication

- Use informal pencil and paper methods to support, record or explain multiplications.
- Extend written methods to long multiplication of a three-digit by a two-digit integer.

Resources

Provide each child with the following:
- a copy of Activity 15 pupil sheet
- a pencil
- a coloured pencil
- a calculator (optional)

Key words

zero, one, two...one hundred thousand   multiply

Say to the children:

Listen carefully.

I am going to tell you some things to do.

I will say them only once, so listen very carefully.

Do only the things you are told to do and nothing else.

If you make a mistake, cross it out. Do not use an eraser.

There are 14 parts to this activity.

The activity

1. Look at the numbers in the grid at the top of the sheet. Colour the numbers 41 and 532 and multiply these two numbers together.

2. Now look at the answer you have just worked out. Write this number beside number one in the grid at the bottom of the sheet. Make sure that you write each digit in a box of its own.

3. Look at the numbers in the grid at the top of the sheet. Colour the numbers 818 and 26 and multiply these two numbers together.

4. Now look at the answer you have just worked out. Write this number beside number two in the grid at the bottom of the sheet. Make sure that you write each digit in a box of its own.

5. Look at the numbers in the grid at the top of the sheet. Colour the numbers 77 and 936 and multiply these two numbers together.

6. Now look at the answer you have just worked out. Write this number beside number three in the grid at the bottom of the sheet. Make sure that you write each digit in a box of its own.

7. Write your name in the ring at the bottom of the sheet.

8. Look at the numbers in the grid at the top of the sheet. Colour the numbers 406 and 58 and multiply these two numbers together.

9. Now look at the answer you have just worked out. Write this number beside number four in the grid at the bottom of the sheet. Make sure that you write each digit in a box of its own.

10. Look at the numbers in the grid at the top of the sheet. Colour the numbers 642 and 31 and multiply these two numbers together.

11. Now look at the answer you have just worked out. Write this number beside number five in the grid at the bottom of the sheet. Make sure that you write each digit in a box of its own.

12. Look at the numbers in the grid at the top of the sheet. Colour the numbers 65 and 207 and multiply these two numbers together.

13. Now look at the answer you have just worked out. Write this number beside number six in the grid at the bottom of the sheet. Make sure that you write each digit in a box of its own.

14. Look at the digits in the grey boxes in the grid at the bottom of the sheet. Working from top to bottom, write these digits out as a six-digit number in the star beside the grid.

Answers

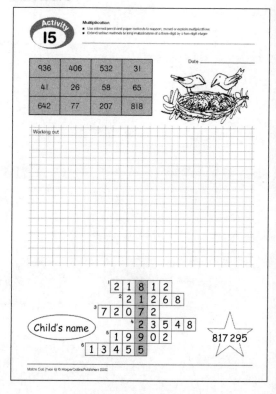

Discussion questions

↓ Look at the grid at the bottom of the sheet. Tell me one of the five-digit numbers you wrote down.

↓ Tell me a digit you wrote in one of the grey boxes. (8, 1, 7, 2, 9, 5)

■ Where on the grid at the bottom of the sheet did you write the number 72 072? (3)

■ Look at your working out. Choose a calculation and tell me how you worked it out. Did anyone work it out a different way?

↑ What number did you write in the star? (817 295)

↑ Which method did you use to work out these calculations?

Activity 15

Multiplication

- Use informal pencil and paper methods to support, record or explain multiplications.
- Extend written methods to long multiplication of a three-digit by a two-digit integer.

Date _____

936	406	532	31
41	26	58	65
642	77	207	818

Working out

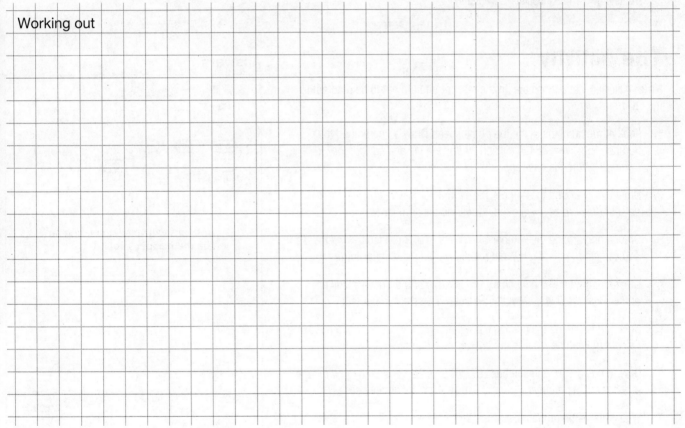

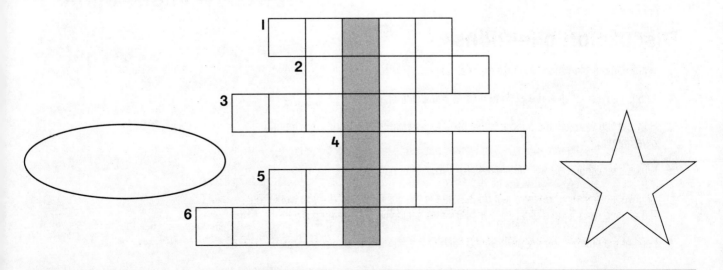

Year 6 Calculations

Division

- Use informal pencil and paper methods to support, record or explain divisions.
- Extend written methods to short division of TU or HTU by U (mixed-number answer).

Resources

Provide each child with the following:
- a copy of Activity 16 pupil sheet
- a pencil
- a calculator (optional)

You will also need a 0 – 9 die

Key words

zero, one, two…one thousand   divided by

Say to the children:

Listen carefully.

I am going to tell you some things to do.

I will say them only once, so listen very carefully.

Do only the things you are told to do and nothing else.

If you make a mistake, cross it out. Do not use an eraser.

There are 7 parts to this activity.

The activity

Note: Italicised instructions are for the teacher and are not to be read out to the children.

1. Look at the numbers at the top of the sheet. Draw a ring around the number 456. What is 456 divided by *(roll the die and call out the number)*? Write the answer on die number one.

2. Draw a ring around the number 88. What is 88 divided by *(roll the die and call out the number)*? Write the answer on die number two.

3. Draw a ring around the number 678. What is 678 divided by *(roll the die and call out the number)*? Write the answer on die number three.

4. Draw a ring around the number 365. What is 365 divided by *(roll the die and call out the number)*? Write the answer on die number four.

5. Draw a ring around the number 72. What is 72 divided by *(roll the die and call out the number)*? Write the answer on die number five.

6. Draw a ring around the number 297. What is 297 divided by *(roll the die and call out the number)*? Write the answer on die number six.

7. Write your name above the words 'Working out'.

Answers

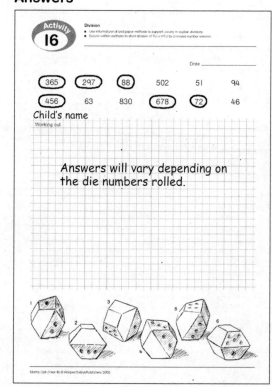

Discussion questions

↓ What number did you write on die number four?

↓ Choose a calculation and explain to us how you worked it out.

■ How did you work out the answer in die number two/five? Did anyone work it out a different way?

■ Which calculations did you find easy/hard? Why?

↑ Choose a calculation you have just done. What is the answer? How did you work it out? Did anyone work it out a different way? How else could you have worked it out?

↑ Look at the numbers on the dice. Round each of these numbers to the nearest 10/100.

Division

- Use informal pencil and paper methods to support, record or explain divisions.
- Extend written methods to short division of TU or HTU by U (mixed-number answer).

Date _____

365	297	88	502	51	94
456	63	830	678	72	46

Working out

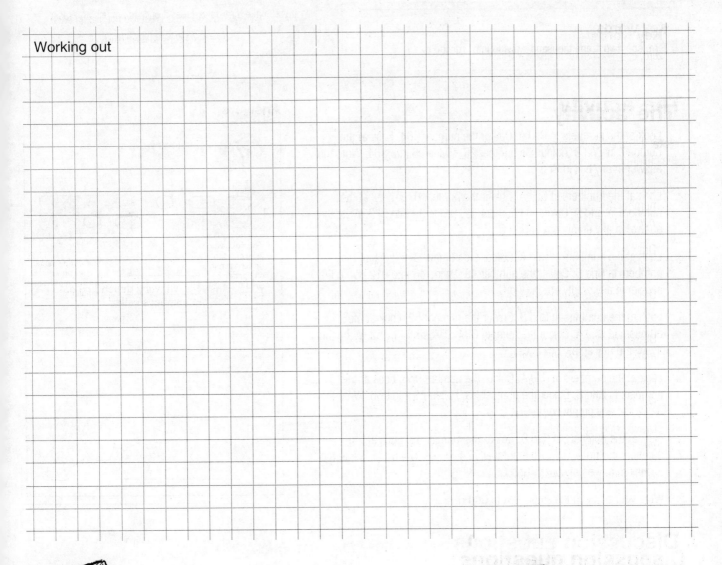

Division

- Use informal pencil and paper methods to support, record or explain divisions.
- Extend written methods to division of HTU by TU (long division, whole-number answer).

Resources

Provide each child with the following:
- a copy of Activity 17 pupil sheet
- a coloured pencil
- a pencil
- a calculator (optional)

Key words

zero, one, two…one thousand   divide into   divide by

Say to the children:

Listen carefully.

I am going to tell you some things to do.

I will say them only once, so listen very carefully.

Do only the things you are told to do and nothing else.

If you make a mistake, cross it out. Do not use an eraser.

There are 7 parts to this activity.

The activity

1. Look at the numbers in Grid A. Colour the number 364. Look at the numbers in Grid B. Colour the number 26. Divide 26 into 364. Write the answer in any box in Grid C.

2. Look at the numbers in Grid A. Colour the number 672. Look at the numbers in Grid B. Colour the number 32. Divide 32 into 672. Write the answer in any empty box in Grid C.

3. Look at the numbers in Grid A. Colour the number 912. Look at the numbers in Grid B. Colour the number 48. Divide 48 into 912. Write the answer in any empty box in Grid C.

4. Look at the numbers in Grid B. Colour the number 52. Look at the numbers in Grid A. Colour the number 884. Divide 884 by 52. Write the answer in any empty box in Grid C.

5. Look at the numbers in Grid A. Colour the number 966. Look at the numbers in Grid B. Colour the number 23. Divide 23 into 966. Write the answer in any empty box in Grid C.

6. Look at the numbers in Grid B. Colour the number 43. Look at the numbers in Grid A. Colour the number 774. Divide 774 by 43. Write the answer in any empty box in Grid C.

7. Write your name in the empty box in Grid C.

Answers

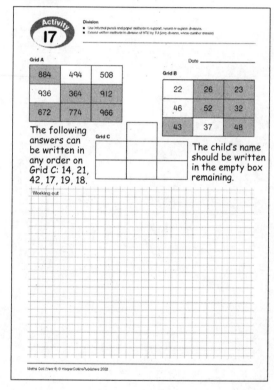

Discussion questions

↓ Tell me a number you wrote in Grid C.

↓ Choose a calculation and tell me how you worked it out.

■ What is 884 divided by 52? (17)

■ What did you find easy/difficult about this activity?

↑ Look at the numbers you did not colour in Grids A and B. Choose any number from each grid and divide the number from Grid B into the number from Grid A. Approximately what is the answer?

↑ Did you make any mistakes? Do you know why you made this mistake? What will you do next time?

Activity 17

Division
- Use informal pencil and paper methods to support, record or explain divisions.
- Extend written methods to division of HTU by TU (long division, whole-number answer).

Grid A

884	494	508
936	364	912
672	774	966

Date _____

Grid B

22	26	23
46	52	32
43	37	48

Grid C

Working out

Year 6 Calculations

Division

■ Use informal pencil and paper methods to support, record or explain divisions.
■ Extend written methods to short division of numbers involving decimals.

Resources

Provide each child with the following:
■ a copy of Activity 18 pupil sheet
■ a pencil
■ a calculator (optional)

Key words

zero, one, two…one thousand   divided by   divided into
decimal   point

Say to the children:

Listen carefully.

I am going to tell you some things to do.

I will say them only once, so listen very carefully.

Do only the things you are told to do and nothing else.

If you make a mistake, cross it out. Do not use an eraser.

There are 7 parts to this activity.

The activity

1. Look at the computer disks. Find the number 49.8. What is 49.8 divided by six? Write the answer on computer number one.

2. Look at the computer disks. Find the number 73.6. What is 73.6 divided by four? Write the answer on computer number two.

3. Look at the computer disks. Find the number 172.5. What is five divided into 172.5? Write the answer on computer number three.

4. Look at the computer disks. Find the number 87.32. What is four divided into 87.32? Write the answer on computer number four.

5. Write your name on computer number five.

6. Look at the computer disks. Find the number 301.07. What is 301.07 divided by seven? Write the answer on computer number six.

7. Look at the computer disks. Find the number 245.97. What is nine divided into 245.97? Write the answer on computer number seven.

Answers

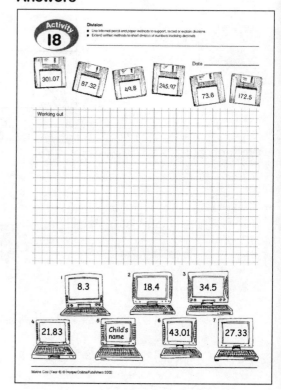

Discussion questions

↓ Tell me one of your answers.

↓ Look at your working out for one of the questions and tell me what you did.

■ What number did you write on computer number two? (18.4)

■ Choose a calculation and explain to us how you worked it out.

↑ How can you check to see if your answers are correct? (e.g. approximate, check with the inverse operation)

↑ Look at each of the numbers on the computers. Round each of these to the nearest whole number. (8.3 – 8; 18.4 – 18; 34.5 – 35; 21.83 – 22; 43.01 – 43; 27.33 – 27)

Activity 18

Division
■ Use informal pencil and paper methods to support, record or explain divisions.
■ Extend written methods to short division of numbers involving decimals.

Date _____

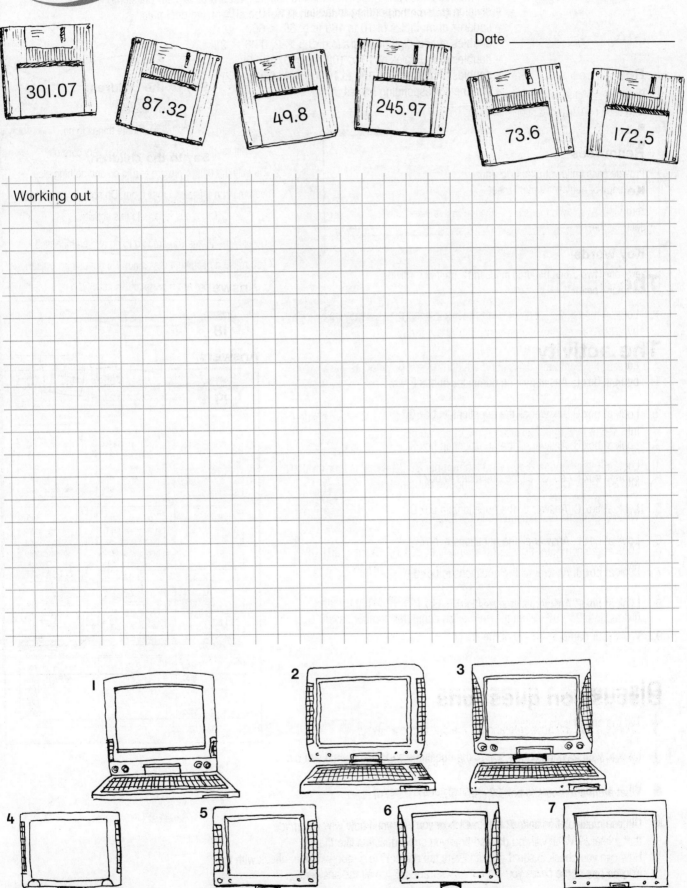

301.07   87.32   49.8   245.97   73.6   172.5

Working out

1   2   3

4   5   6   7

Multiplication and division

- Derive quickly:
  - division facts corresponding to tables up to 10 × 10;
  - squares of multiples of 10 to 100 (e.g. 60 × 60);
  - doubles of two-digit numbers (e.g. 3.8 × 2, 0.76 × 2);
  - doubles of multiples of 10 to 1000 (e.g. 670 × 2);
  - doubles of multiples of 100 to 10 000 (e.g. 6500 × 2);
  - and the corresponding halves.

Resources

Provide each child with the following:
- a copy of Activity 19 pupil sheet
- a pencil

Key words

zero, one, two…one hundred thousand   multiply   divide
decimal   point

Say to the children:

Listen carefully.

I am going to tell you some things to do.

I will say them only once, so listen very carefully.

Do only the things you are told to do and nothing else.

If you make a mistake, cross it out. Do not use an eraser.

There are 9 parts to this activity.

The activity

1. Look at box E. Answer all the questions in box E.

2. Look at box G. Answer all the questions in box G.

3. Look at box B. Answer all the questions in box B.

4. Look at box I. Answer all the questions in box I.

5. Look at box C. Answer all the questions in box C.

6. Look at box L. Answer all the questions in box L.

7. Look at box J. Answer all the questions in box J.

8. Look at box F. Answer all the questions in box F.

9. Write your name at the top of the sheet.

Discussion questions

↓ Choose a box you answered and tell me one of the answers.

↓ Which question in box G has an answer of eight? (48 ÷ 6)

■ What are the answers to box C? (100, 58, 0.47, 7, 470)

■ Did you make any mistakes? If so, which one(s)? Do you know why you made that mistake? What will you do next time you see a question like that?

↑ Choose one of the boxes you did not answer and tell me all the answers.

↑ Choose a box you have already answered and explain to us how you worked out the answers.

Answers

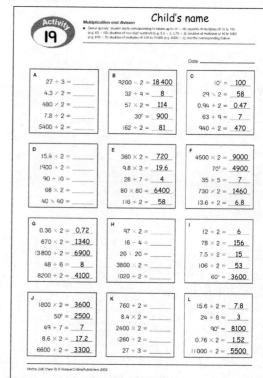

Activity 19

Multiplication and division

■ Derive quickly: division facts corresponding to tables up to 10 × 10; squares of multiples of 10 to 100 (e.g. 60 × 60); doubles of two-digit numbers (e.g. 3.8 × 2, 0.76 × 2); doubles of multiples of 10 to 1000 (e.g. 670 × 2); doubles of multiples of 100 to 10 000 (e.g. 6500 × 2); and the corresponding halves.

Date _____

A

$27 \div 3 =$ _____

$4.3 \times 2 =$ _____

$480 \times 2 =$ _____

$7.8 \div 2 =$ _____

$5400 \div 2 =$ _____

B

$9200 \times 2 =$ _____

$32 \div 4 =$ _____

$57 \times 2 =$ _____

$30^2 =$ _____

$162 \div 2 =$ _____

C

$10^2 =$ _____

$29 \times 2 =$ _____

$0.94 \div 2 =$ _____

$63 \div 9 =$ _____

$940 \div 2 =$ _____

D

$15.4 \div 2 =$ _____

$1900 \div 2 =$ _____

$90 \div 10 =$ _____

$68 \times 2 =$ _____

$40 \times 40 =$ _____

E

$360 \times 2 =$ _____

$9.8 \times 2 =$ _____

$28 \div 7 =$ _____

$80 \times 80 =$ _____

$116 \div 2 =$ _____

F

$4500 \times 2 =$ _____

$70^2 =$ _____

$35 \div 5 =$ _____

$730 \times 2 =$ _____

$13.6 \div 2 =$ _____

G

$0.36 \times 2 =$ _____

$670 \times 2 =$ _____

$13\,800 \div 2 =$ _____

$48 \div 6 =$ _____

$8200 \div 2 =$ _____

H

$97 \times 2 =$ _____

$16 \div 4 =$ _____

$20 \times 20 =$ _____

$3800 \times 2 =$ _____

$1020 \div 2 =$ _____

I

$12 \div 2 =$ _____

$78 \times 2 =$ _____

$7.5 \times 2 =$ _____

$106 \div 2 =$ _____

$60^2 =$ _____

J

$1800 \times 2 =$ _____

$50^2 =$ _____

$49 \div 7 =$ _____

$8.6 \times 2 =$ _____

$6600 \div 2 =$ _____

K

$760 \div 2 =$ _____

$8.4 \times 2 =$ _____

$2400 \times 2 =$ _____

$1260 \div 2 =$ _____

$27 \div 3 =$ _____

L

$15.6 \div 2 =$ _____

$24 \div 8 =$ _____

$90^2 =$ _____

$0.76 \times 2 =$ _____

$11\,000 \div 2 =$ _____

Activity 20

Year 6 Calculations

Multiplication and division

■ Use known number facts and place value to consolidate mental multiplication and division.

Resources

Provide each child with the following:
■ a copy of Activity 20 pupil sheet
■ a pencil

Key words

zero, one, two…one hundred answer calculation decimal point times multiplied by lots of groups of product

Say to the children:

Listen carefully.

I am going to tell you some things to do.

I will say them only once, so listen very carefully.

Do only the things you are told to do and nothing else.

If you make a mistake, cross it out. Do not use an eraser.

There are 16 parts to this activity.

The activity

1. Write your name at the top of the sheet.

2. Find calculation five. Work out the answer and write it in the circle.

3. Now find the same number in one of the grey boxes at the top of the sheet.

4. In this box there is a letter. Write this letter in box one at the bottom of the sheet.

5. Find calculation six. Work out the answer and write it in the circle. Now write the letter to the answer to calculation six in boxes 18 and 22.

6. Find calculation three. Work out the answer and write it in the circle. Now write the letter to the answer to calculation three in box four.

7. Find calculation four. Work out the answer and write it in the circle. Now write the letter to the answer to calculation four in boxes 15 and 25.

8. Find calculation 13. Work out the answer and write it in the circle. Now write the letter to the answer to calculation 13 in boxes 10, 19 and 26.

9. Find calculation one. Work out the answer and write it in the circle. Now write the letter to the answer to calculation one in boxes 13 and 17.

10. Find calculation two. Work out the answer and write it in the circle. Now write the letter to the answer to calculation two in boxes nine and 21.

11. Find calculation 12. Work out the answer and write it in the circle. Now write the letter to the answer to calculation 12 in boxes three, 14 and 23.

12. Find calculation eight. Work out the answer and write it in the circle. Now write the letter to the answer to calculation eight in box 24.

13. Find calculation seven. Work out the answer and write it in the circle. Now write the letter to the answer to calculation seven in box five.

14. Find calculation nine. Work out the answer and write it in the circle. Now write the letter to the answer to calculation nine in boxes seven and 16.

15. Find calculation 11. Work out the answer and write it in the circle. Now write the letter to the answer to calculation 11 in boxes eight and 12.

16. Find calculation 10. Work out the answer and write it in the circle. Write the letter to the answer to calculation 10 in boxes two, 11 and 20.

Answers

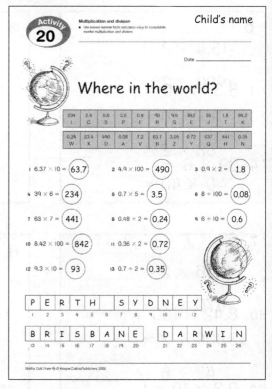

Discussion questions

↓ Where in the world are we? (Australia)

↓ Tell me the answer to one of the calculations.

■ What happens to a decimal when you multiply it by 10/100? (The digits move one/two places to the left.) What happens to a decimal when you divide it by 10/100? (The digits move one/two places to the right.)

■ Look at all the calculations on the sheet. Which calculations do you find easy/hard?

↑ Choose a calculation you did and explain how you worked it out. Did anyone work out this calculation in a different way?

↑ Tell me another multiplication/division calculation that is not on the sheet.

Activity 20

Multiplication and division

■ Use known number facts and place value to consolidate mental multiplication and division.

Date _____

Where in the world?

234	2.4	0.6	3.5	0.8	93	9.4	842	35	1.8	84.2
I	C	S	P	F	R	G	E	J	T	K

0.24	23.4	490	0.08	7.2	63.7	3.05	0.72	637	441	0.35
W	X	D	A	V	B	Z	Y	Q	H	N

1 $6.37 \times 10 =$ ◯

2 $4.9 \times 100 =$ ◯

3 $0.9 \times 2 =$ ◯

4 $39 \times 6 =$ ◯

5 $0.7 \times 5 =$ ◯

6 $8 \div 100 =$ ◯

7 $63 \times 7 =$ ◯

8 $0.48 \div 2 =$ ◯

9 $6 \div 10 =$ ◯

10 $8.42 \times 100 =$ ◯

11 $0.36 \times 2 =$ ◯

12 $9.3 \times 10 =$ ◯

13 $0.7 \div 2 =$ ◯

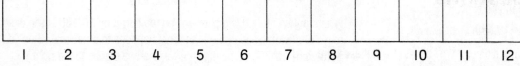

| 1 | 2 | 3 | 4 | 5 | 6 | 7 | 8 | 9 | 10 | 11 | 12 |

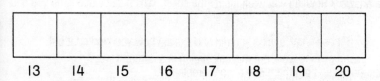

| 13 | 14 | 15 | 16 | 17 | 18 | 19 | 20 |

| 21 | 22 | 23 | 24 | 25 | 26 |

Year 6 Solving problems

Problems involving 'real life' and measures

- Identify and use appropriate operations (including combinations of operations) to solve word problems involving numbers and quantities based on 'real life' and measures (including time), using one or more steps.
- Explain methods and reasoning.

Resources

Provide each child with the following:

- a copy of Activity 21 pupil sheet
- a pencil
- a calculator (optional)
- working out paper (optional)

Key words

zero, one, two…ten thousand   altogether   per cent   area
metre   kilometre   mile   hour   minute

Say to the children:

Listen carefully.

I am going to tell you some things to do.

I will say them only once, so listen very carefully.

Do only the things you are told to do and nothing else.

If you make a mistake, cross it out. Do not use an eraser.

There are 13 parts to this activity.

The activity

1. Look at card one. Work out the answer and write it in box eight.

2. Look at card two. Work out the answer and write it in box six.

3. Look at card five. Work out the answer and write it in box two.

4. Look at card 13. Work out the answer and write it in box 13.

5. Look at card nine. Work out the answer and write it in box 11.

6. Look at card four. Work out the answer and write it in box one.

7. Write your name in box 10.

8. Look at card three. Work out the answer and write it in box nine.

9. Look at card 12. Work out the answer and write it in box five.

10. Look at card seven. Work out the answer and write it in box three.

11. Look at card 14. Work out the answer and write it in box 12.

12. Look at card 10. Work out the answer and write it in box seven.

13. Look at card six. Work out the answer and write it in box four.

Answers

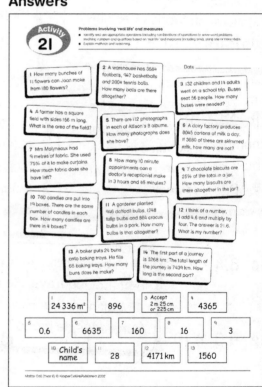

Discussion questions

↓ What did you write in box 11? (28)

↓ Which questions did you find difficult? Why do you think these were hard?

■ Choose one of the word problems you solved. What is the answer? How did you work it out?
  Did anyone work it out a different way?

■ What is the answer to card 14? (4171 km)

↑ Choose two or more of the numbers you have written in the boxes and put them into a word problem.

↑ Which questions did you not answer? (8/11) What are the answers to these questions? (22/3058)

Activity 21

Problems involving 'real life' and measures

- Identify and use appropriate operations (including combinations of operations) to solve word problems involving numbers and quantities based on 'real life' and measures (including time), using one or more steps.
- Explain methods and reasoning.

Date _____

1 How many bunches of 11 flowers can Joan make from 180 flowers?

2 A warehouse has 3684 footballs, 947 basketballs and 2004 tennis balls. How many balls are there altogether?

3 132 children and 14 adults went on a school trip. Buses seat 56 people. How many buses were needed?

4 A farmer has a square field with sides 156 m long. What is the area of the field?

5 There are 112 photographs in each of Allison's 8 albums. How many photographs does she have?

6 A dairy factory produces 8045 cartons of milk a day. If 3680 of these are skimmed milk, how many are not?

7 Mrs Molyneaux had 9 metres of fabric. She used 75% of it to make curtains. How much fabric does she have left?

8 How many 10 minute appointments can a doctor's receptionist make in 3 hours and 45 minutes?

9 7 chocolate biscuits are 25% of the total in a jar. How many biscuits are there altogether in the jar?

10 760 candles are put into 19 boxes. There are the same number of candles in each box. How many candles are there in 4 boxes?

11 A gardener planted 946 daffodil bulbs, 1248 tulip bulbs and 864 crocus bulbs in a park. How many bulbs is that altogether?

12 I think of a number, I add 4.8 and multiply by four. The answer is 21.6. What is my number?

13 A baker puts 24 buns onto baking trays. He fills 65 baking trays. How many buns does he make?

14 The first part of a journey is 3268 km. The total length of the journey is 7439 km. How long is the second part?

1	2	3	4

5	6	7	8	9

10	11	12	13

Maths Call (Year 6) © HarperCollins*Publishers* 2002

Problems involving money

- Identify and use appropriate operations (including combinations of operations) to solve word problems involving numbers and quantities based on money, using one or more steps, including converting pounds to foreign currency, or vice versa, and calculating percentages such as VAT.
- Explain methods and reasoning.

Resources

Provide each child with the following:
- a copy of Activity 22 pupil sheet
- a pencil
- a calculator (optional)

Key words

zero, one, two…ten thousand   pounds   pence   total   cost   shared equally   per cent   change   spend   priced at

Say to the children:

Listen carefully.

I am going to tell you some things to do.

I will say them only once, so listen very carefully.

Do only the things you are told to do and nothing else.

If you make a mistake, cross it out. Do not use an eraser.

There are 11 parts to this activity.

The activity

1. What is the total of £140, £5.57 and £12.09? Write the answer on note one.

2. What is the cost of 168 chocolate bars at 27p each? Write the answer on note two.

3. Four people won £16 848 to be shared equally between them. How much does each person get? Write the answer on note three.

4. Write your name on note four.

5. The estate agent's fee for selling a house is five per cent. Calculate the fee on a house sold for £120 000. Write the answer on note five.

6. 568 people attend a concert. Each ticket costs £35. What is the total cost of all the tickets? Write the answer on note six.

7. Tornado Bars cost 47p. How much does it cost to buy 15? Write the answer on note seven.

8. There are 1.7 euros to the pound. What is the price in pounds for a holiday costing 6800 euros? Write the answer on note eight.

9. VAT is 17.5 per cent. What is the total cost of a stereo priced at £390 before VAT? Write the answer on note nine.

10. Mrs Herne's shopping bill comes to £37.42. What change does she receive from £50? Write the answer on note 10.

11. Valda's mum had £69.73 in her purse. After her shopping trip she had £24.49 left. How much money did she spend? Write the answer on note 11.

Answers

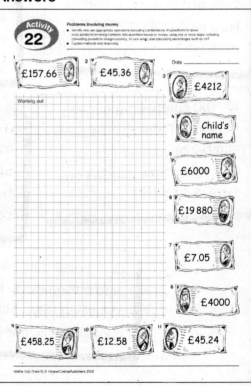

Discussion questions

↓ Tell me one of the answers you wrote down.

↓ Look at your working out. Choose a problem you worked out and explain to us what you did.

■ Choose one of the word problems you solved. What is the answer? How did you work it out? Did anyone work it out a different way?

■ What is the answer on note three? (£4212)

↑ VAT is 17.5 per cent of the price of an item. What is the total cost of a stereo priced at £390 before VAT? What is the answer? (£458.25) How did you work it out? Did anyone work it out using a different method?

↑ Look at all the answers you have written down. Round each amount to the nearest pound. (1. £157.66 = £158 2. £45.36 = £45 3. £4212 = £4212 5. £6000 = £6000 6. £19 880 = £19 880 7. £7.05 = £7 8. £4000 = £4000 9. £458.25 = £458 10. £12.58 = £13 11. £45.24 = £45)

Problems involving money

- Identify and use appropriate operations (including combinations of operations) to solve word problems involving numbers and quantities based on money, using one or more steps, including converting pounds to foreign currency, or vice versa, and calculating percentages such as VAT.
- Explain methods and reasoning.

Date _____

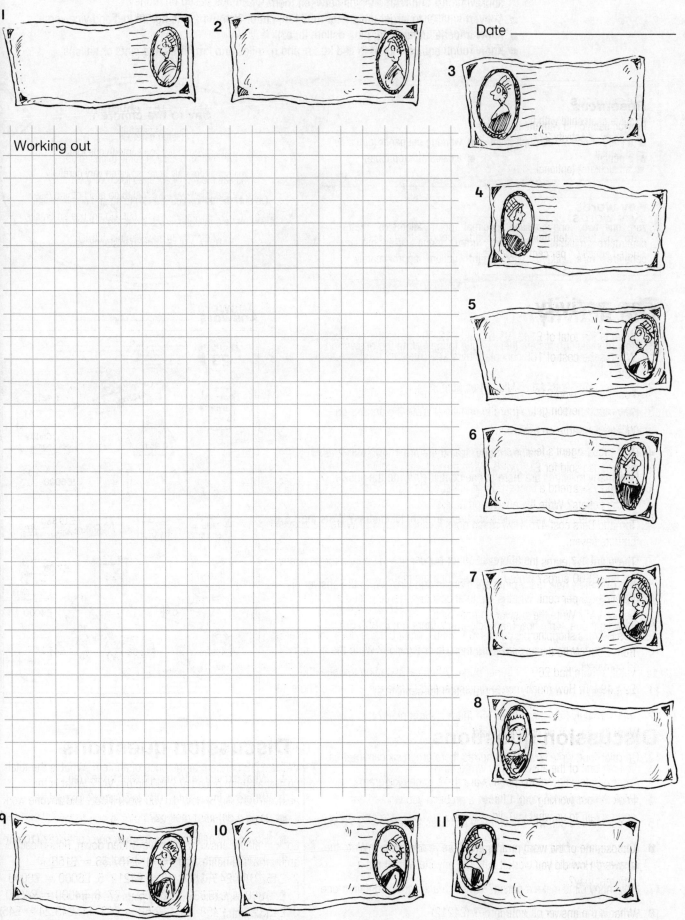

Working out

Year 6 Measures

Length, mass and capacity

- Use, read and write standard metric units (km, m, cm, mm, kg, g, l, ml, cl), including their abbreviations, and relationships between them.
- Convert smaller to larger units (e.g. m to km, cm or mm to m, g to kg, ml to l) and vice versa.
- Know imperial units (mile, pint, gallon, lb, oz).
- Know rough equivalents of lb and kg, oz and g, miles and km, litres and pints or gallons.

Resources

Provide each child with the following:
- a copy of Activity 23 pupil sheet
- working out paper (optional)
- a pencil
- a calculator (optional)

Key words

zero, one, two…one thousand decimal point kilometre metre centimetre millimetre kilogram gram tonne litre millilitre centilitre mile pound ounce pint gallon approximately

Say to the children:

Listen carefully.

I am going to tell you some things to do.

I will say them only once, so listen very carefully.

Do only the things you are told to do and nothing else.

If you make a mistake, cross it out. Do not use an eraser.

There are 18 parts to this activity.

The activity

1. How many kilograms are there in one tonne? Write the answer on weight two.

2. On ruler one, write 4.125 kilometres in metres.

3. How many centilitres are there in one litre? Write the answer on container four.

4. On container two, write how many litres there are in 400 millilitres.

5. How many millilitres are there in one centilitre? Write the answer on container five.

6. Approximately how many miles are there in eight kilometres? Write the answer on ruler two.

7. On weight five, write the abbreviation for ounce.

8. Approximately how many pints are there in one litre? Write the answer on container seven.

9. On weight one, write how many kilograms there are in 850 grams.

10. Approximately how many litres are there in one gallon? Write the answer on container six.

11. On container three, write the abbreviation for centilitres.

12. Approximately how many litres are there in eight pints? Write the answer on container nine.

13. On ruler four, write how many metres there are in six centimetres.

14. Approximately how many pounds are there in one kilogram? Write the answer on weight three.

15. On container eight, write how many millilitres there are in 3.25 litres.

16. Approximately how many grams are there in one ounce? Write the answer on weight four.

17. How many pints make a gallon? Write the answer on container one.

18. Write your name on ruler three.

Answers

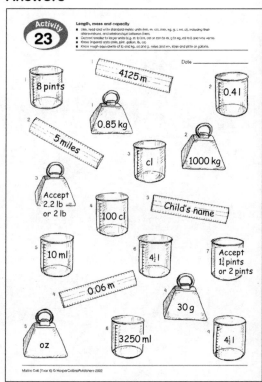

Discussion questions

↓ What did you write in container three? (cl)

↓ Where did you write 1000 kilograms? (weight 2)

■ How many kilograms are there in one tonne? (1000 kg)

■ How many millilitres are there in one centilitre? (10 ml)

↑ Approximately how many kilometres are there in 30 miles? (48 km)

↑ Approximately how many pints are there in 18 litres? (32 pints)

Length, mass and capacity

- Use, read and write standard metric units (km, m, cm, mm, kg, g, l, ml, cl), including their abbreviations, and relationships between them.
- Convert smaller to larger units (e.g. m to km, cm or mm to m, g to kg, ml to l) and vice versa.
- Know imperial units (mile, pint, gallon, lb, oz).
- Know rough equivalents of lb and kg, oz and g, miles and km, litres and pints or gallons.

Date _____

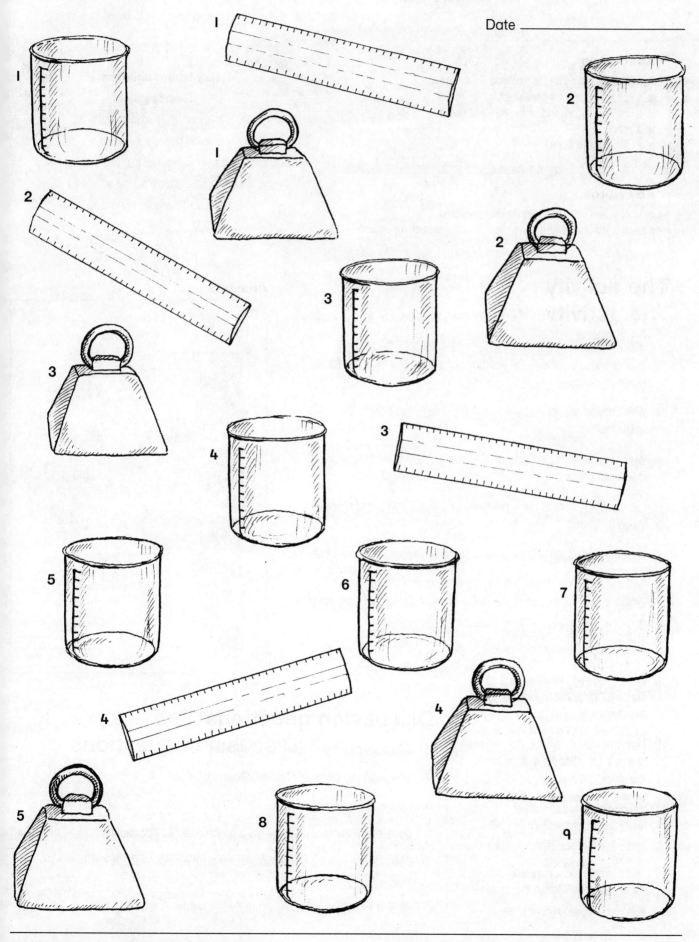

Area and perimeter

■ Calculate the perimeter and area of simple compound shapes that can be split into rectangles.

Resources

Provide each child with the following:

■ a copy of Activity 24 pupil sheet
■ a red, blue, green and yellow coloured pencil
■ a pencil
■ a calculator (optional)

Key words

zero, one, two…ten hundred   area   perimeter
square centimetre (cm²)   square metre (m²)   centimetre   metre

Say to the children:

Listen carefully.

I am going to tell you some things to do.

I will say them only once, so listen very carefully.

Do only the things you are told to do and nothing else.

If you make a mistake, cross it out. Do not use an eraser.

There are 12 parts to this activity.

The activity

1. Look at shape A. What is the area of shape A? Write the answer inside the shape.

2. Look at shape B. What is the perimeter of shape B? Write the answer inside the shape.

3. Which shape has an area of 110 square centimetres? Colour that shape red.

4. Which shape has a perimeter of 108 centimetres? Write the answer inside that shape.

5. Look at shape F. What is the perimeter of shape F? Write the answer inside the shape.

6. Look at shape C. What is the area of shape C? Write the answer inside the shape.

7. Which shape has an area of 26 square metres? Colour that shape blue.

8. Which shape has a perimeter of 42 centimetres? Colour that shape green.

9. Look at shape E. What is the area of shape E? Write the answer inside the shape.

10. Look at shape D. What is the perimeter of shape D? Write the answer inside the shape.

11. Which shape has an area of 1422 square metres? Write your name inside that shape.

12. Which shape has a perimeter of 54 centimetres? Colour that shape yellow.

Answers

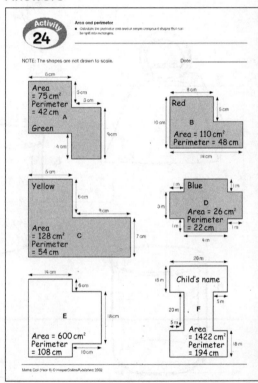

Discussion questions

↓ Which shape did you colour blue? (D)

↓ Where did you write your name? (Shape F)

■ What is the perimeter of shape E? (108 cm) What is the area of shape A? (75 cm²)

■ Choose any shape and tell me the area/perimeter of that shape.

↑ Which shape has the largest/smallest area? (F/D) Which shape has the largest/smallest perimeter? (F/A)

↑ What is the difference in the perimeters of shapes A and B? (6 cm)

Area and perimeter

■ Calculate the perimeter and area of simple compound shapes that can be split into rectangles.

NOTE: The shapes are not drawn to scale.

Date _____

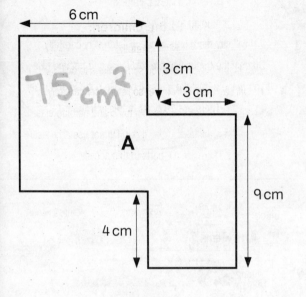

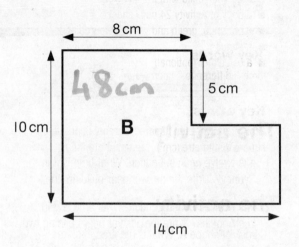

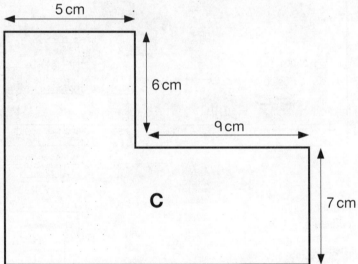

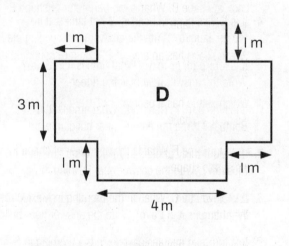

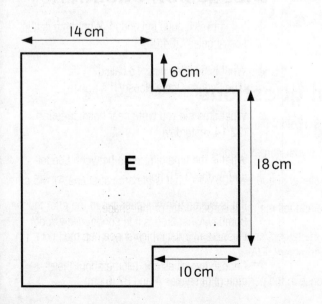

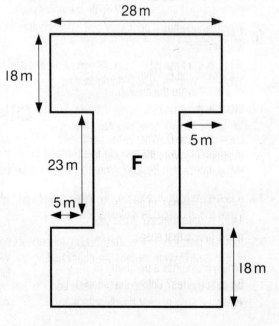

Maths Call (Year 6) © HarperCollins*Publishers* 2002

Year 6 Measures

Time
■ Appreciate different times around the world.

Resources

Provide each child with the following:
■ a copy of Activity 25 pupil sheet
■ a pencil

Key words

time   difference   noon   a.m.   p.m.

Say to the children:

Listen carefully.

I am going to tell you some things to do.

I will say them only once, so listen very carefully.

Do only the things you are told to do and nothing else.

If you make a mistake, cross it out. Do not use an eraser.

There are 16 parts to this activity.

The activity

1. It is twelve noon in London. What time is it in Sydney? Write the answer near building one.

2. It is twelve noon in London. What time is it in Los Angeles? Write the answer near building two.

3. It is twelve noon in London. What time is it in Beijing? Write the answer near building seven.

4. It is twelve noon in London. What time is it in Rio de Janeiro? Write the answer near building eleven.

5. It is four p.m. in Tokyo. What time is it in Cairo? Write the answer near building fifteen.

6. It is nine a.m. in New York. What time is it in Bombay? Write the answer near building eight.

7. It is eight thirty at night in Tokyo. What time is it in Moscow? Write the answer near building three.

8. It is eleven thirty-seven in the morning in Mexico City. What time is it in Cairo? Write the answer near building fourteen.

9. It is fourteen minutes past six in the morning in Sydney. What time is it in Johannesburg? Write the answer near building four.

10. Write your name near building five.

11. What is the time difference between Bombay and New York? Write the answer near building twelve.

12. What is the time difference between London and Los Angeles? Write the answer near building nine.

13. It is five minutes past one in the afternoon in Rio de Janeiro. What time is it in Beijing? Write the answer near building sixteen.

14. It is twelve noon in Mexico city. What time is it in Moscow? Write the answer near building ten.

15. It is half past four in the afternoon in Johannesburg. What time is it in Cairo? Write the answer near building six.

16. What is the time difference between London and Sydney? Write the answer near building thirteen.

Answers

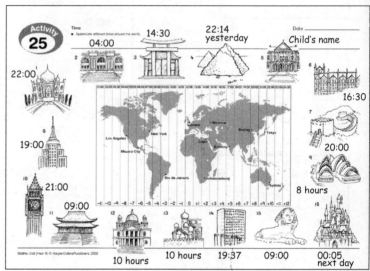

Discussion questions

↓ If it is twelve noon in London. What time is it in Los Angeles? (04:00)

↓ What is building nine/15 called? (The Sydney Opera House/The Sphinx)

■ What time did you write near building four? (22:14 yesterday)

■ What is the time difference between London and Sydney? (10 hours)

↑ If it is eleven minutes past two in the afternoon in Bombay, what time is it in London/New York/Los Angeles/Beijing (09:11/04:11/01:11/17:11)

↑ Choose two cities and tell me about their time difference.

Activity

25

Time

■ Appreciate different times around the world.

1

2

3

4

5

6

7

8

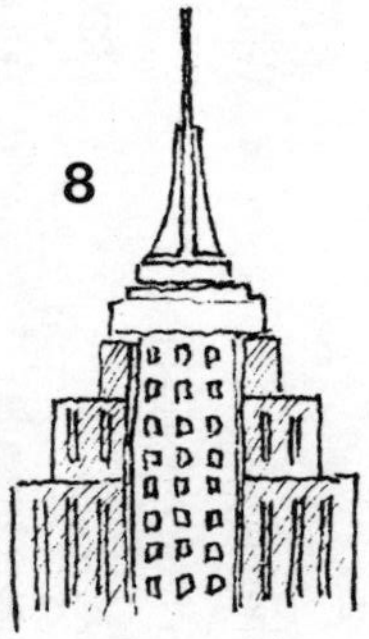

9

10

11

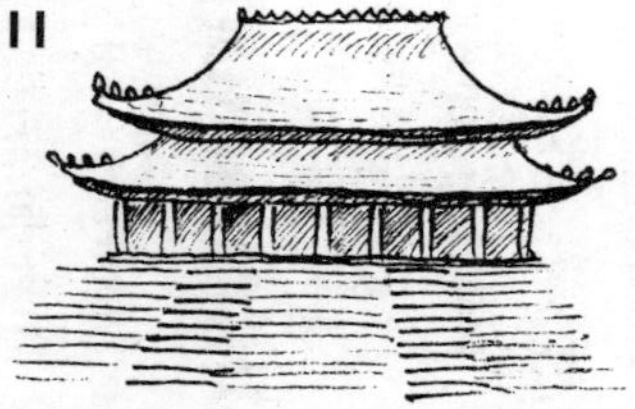

12

13

14

15

16

| −11 | −10 | −9 | −8 | −7 | −6 | −5 | −4 | −3 | −2 | −1 | 0 | +1 | +2 | +3 | +4 | +5 | +6 | +7 | +8 | +9 | +10 | +11 | +12 |

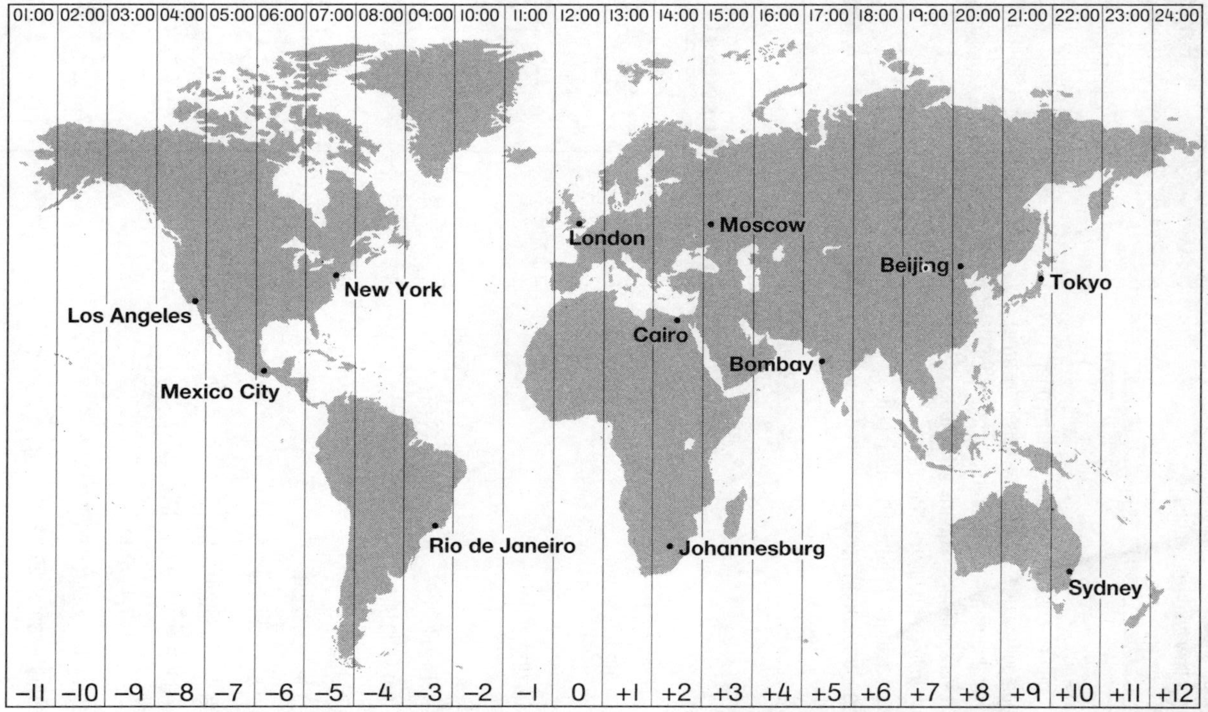

01:00 02:00 03:00 04:00 05:00 06:00 07:00 08:00 09:00 10:00 11:00 12:00 13:00 14:00 15:00 16:00 17:00 18:00 19:00 20:00 21:00 22:00 23:00 24:00

Los Angeles
Mexico City
New York
Rio de Janeiro
London
Moscow
Cairo
Bombay
Johannesburg
Beijing
Tokyo
Sydney

3-D and 2-D shapes

■ Describe and visualise properties of solid shapes such as parallel or perpendicular faces or edges.

■ Classify quadrilaterals, using criteria such as parallel sides, equal angles, equal sides…

Resources

Provide each child with the following:

■ a copy of Activity 26 pupil sheet

■ a red, blue, green and yellow coloured pencil

Key words

3-D (three dimensional) cube cuboid sphere hemisphere cylinder pentagon heptagon cone triangular-based pyramid square-based pyramid tetrahedron polyhedron octahedron dodecahedron 2-D (two dimensional) square rhombus rectangle circle semi-circle equilateral triangle isosceles triangle scalene triangle pentagon hexagon heptagon octagon kite trapezium polygon quadrilateral parallelogram

Say to the children:

Listen carefully.

I am going to tell you some things to do.

I will say them only once, so listen very carefully.

Do only the things you are told to do and nothing else.

If you make a mistake, cross it out. Do not use an eraser.

There are 17 parts to this activity.

The activity

1. Look at all the shapes. Colour the cube red.
2. Draw a red cross inside the heptagon.
3. Colour the rhombus blue.
4. Draw a blue cross inside the square.
5. Colour the kite green.
6. Draw a green cross inside the cone.
7. Colour the dodecahedron yellow.
8. Draw a yellow cross inside the cuboid.
9. Draw a red tick inside the trapezium.
10. Draw a red ring around the equilateral triangle.
11. Draw a blue tick inside the hexagon.
12. Draw a blue ring around the scalene triangle.
13. Draw a green tick inside the tetrahedron.
14. Draw a green ring around the octagon.
15. Draw a yellow tick inside the parallelogram.
16. Draw a yellow ring around the octahedron.
17. Write your name inside the hemisphere.

Answers

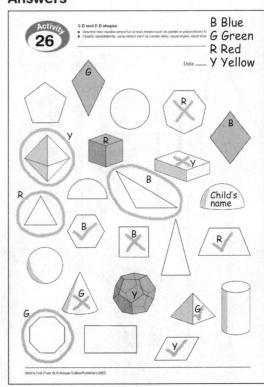

Discussion questions

↓ Which shape did you draw a red cross in? (heptagon)

↓ What did you do to the cone? (drew a green cross inside it)

■ Which shapes did you not do anything to? (rectangle, cylinder, circle, pentagon, semi-circle, isosceles triangle, sphere)

■ Which shapes are quadrilaterals? (square, rectangle, rhombus, parallelogram, trapezium, kite)

↑ Choose a shape and tell me some of its properties.

↑ What is a polygon? (A flat shape with many angles.)
What is a polyhedron? (A solid shape with many faces.)

3-D and 2-D shapes

- Describe and visualise properties of solid shapes such as parallel or perpendicular faces or edges.
- Classify quadrilaterals, using criteria such as parallel sides, equal angles, equal sides...

Date _____

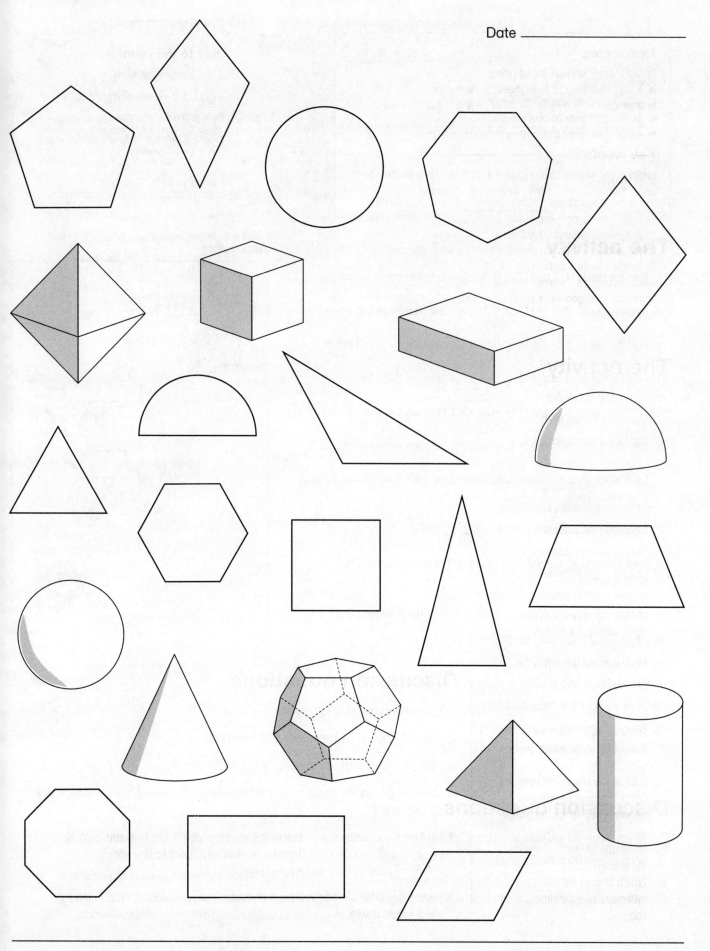

Activity 27

Translation

■ Recognise where a shape will be after two translations.

Resources

Provide each child with the following:
- ■ a copy of Activity 27 pupil sheet
- ■ a pencil
- ■ a ruler
- ■ a coloured pencil

Key words

negative six, negative five, negative four…six co-ordinate point
unit translate left right down up hexagon

Say to the children:

Listen carefully.

I am going to tell you some things to do.

I will say them only once, so listen very carefully.

Do only the things you are told to do and nothing else.

If you make a mistake, cross it out. Do not use an eraser.

There are 15 parts to this activity.

The activity

1. Find the points (1,1) and (2,3). Rule a line between these two points.

2. Find the points (2,3) and (1,5). Rule a line between these two points.

3. Find the points (1,5) and (4,5). Rule a line between these two points.

4. Find the points (4,5) and (5,3). Rule a line between these two points.

5. Find the points (5,3) and (4,1). Rule a line between these two points.

6. Find the points (4,1) and (1,1). Rule a line between these two points.

7. Look at the shape you have just drawn. Using your coloured pencil, lightly shade this shape.

8. Now write the letter A inside the shape.

9. Look at shape A. Translate this shape six units to the left and two units down.

10. Look at the shape you have just drawn. Using your coloured pencil, lightly shade this shape.

11. Now write the letter B inside the shape.

12. Look at shape A again. Translate this shape one unit to the right and six units down.

13. Look at the shape you have just drawn. Using your coloured pencil, lightly shade this shape.

14. Now write the letter C inside the shape.

15. Write your name inside shape C.

Answers

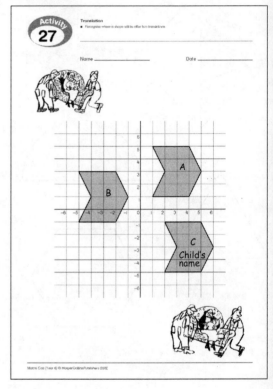

Discussion questions

↓ What have you drawn? (three shapes/hexagons)

↓ What do you call shapes A, B and C? (hexagons)

■ Tell me a co-ordinate for shape C? [(2, −1),(5, −1), (6, −3), (5, −5), (2, −5), (3, −3)]

■ How many units has shape B been translated from shape A? (6 units to the left and 2 units down)

↑ Tell me the co-ordinates for one of the lines in shape B. [(−1, 1) and (−2, 3); (−2, 3) and (−5, 3); (−5, 3) and (−4, 1); (−4, 1) and (−5, −1); (−5, −1) and (−2, −1); (−2, −1) and (−1, 1)]

↑ How many units has shape C been translated from shape B? (7 units to the right and 4 units down)

Activity 27

Translation
■ Recognise where a shape will be after two translations

Name _____   Date _____

						6					
						5					
						4					
						3					
						2					
						1					
–6	–5	–4	–3	–2	–1	0	1	2	3	4	5	6
						–1					
						–2					
						–3					
						–4					
						–5					
						–6					

Year 6 Shape and space

Position and direction

■ Read and plot co-ordinates in all four quadrants.

Resources

Provide each child with the following:
■ a copy of Activity 28 pupil sheet
■ a pencil

Key words

negative six, negative five, negative four…six   co-ordinates
x-axis   *y*-axis   first/second/third/fourth quadrant

Say to the children:

Listen carefully.

I am going to tell you some things to do.

I will say them only once, so listen very carefully.

Do only the things you are told to do and nothing else.

If you make a mistake, cross it out. Do not use an eraser.

There are 20 parts to this activity.

The activity

1. Draw a ring around the co-ordinate (2, 5).

2. Draw a ring around the co-ordinate (−6, 2).

3. Draw a cross at the co-ordinate (−6, 4).

4. Draw a cross at the co-ordinate (−4, 1).

5. Draw a ring around the co-ordinate (−3, −2).

6. Draw a cross at the co-ordinate (3, 6).

7. Draw a cross at the co-ordinate (4, −2).

8. Draw a ring around the co-ordinate (6, −1).

9. Draw a ring around the co-ordinate (−5, 6).

10. Draw a cross at the co-ordinate (−2, −3).

11. Draw a cross at the co-ordinate (4, 2).

12. Draw a ring around the co-ordinate (−5, −3).

13. Draw a ring around the co-ordinate (2, −3).

14. Draw a ring around the co-ordinate (−2, −6).

15. Draw a cross at the co-ordinate (5, −5).

16. Draw a ring around the co-ordinate (6, 3).

17. Draw a cross at the co-ordinate (1, 2).

18. Draw a ring around the co-ordinate (−3, 4).

19. Draw a cross at the co-ordinate (3, −6).

20. Write your name at the top of the sheet.

Answers

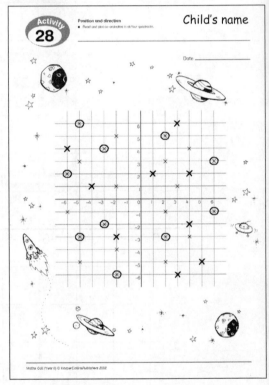

Discussion questions

↓ Tell me a co-ordinate that you drew a ring around.

↓ Tell me a co-ordinate you drew.

■ Did you draw a ring around the co-ordinate (−5, 3)? (no)

■ Which is the *x*-axis/*y*-axis?

↑ Look at all the crosses. Tell me a co-ordinate in the first/second/third/fourth quadrant.

↑ Give me a co-ordinate that does not have a cross at that point. Which quadrant is it in?

Position and direction

■ Read and plot co-ordinates in all four quadrants.

Date _____

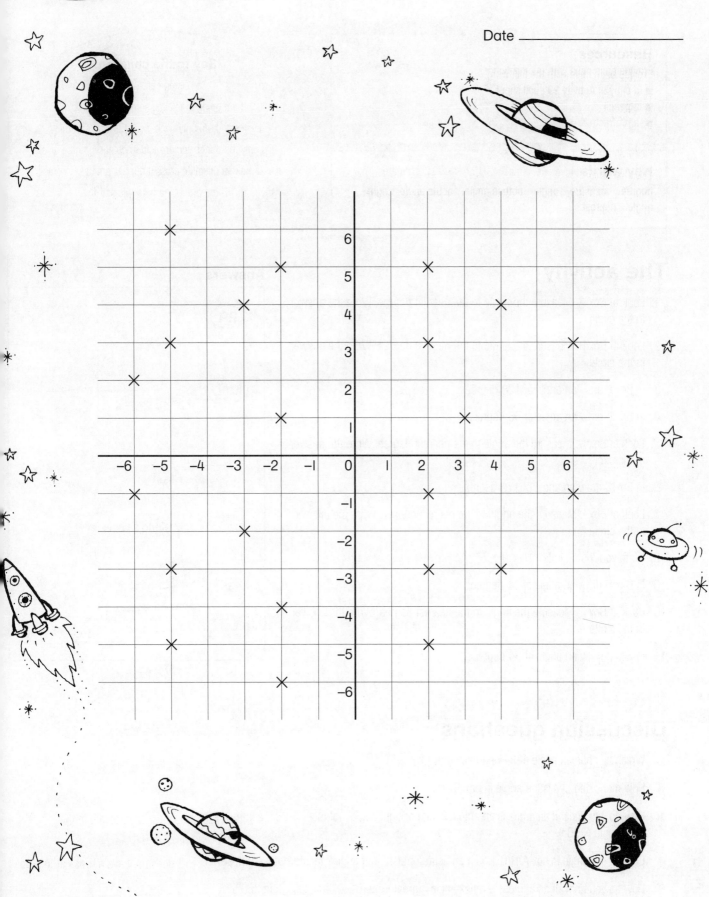

Activity 29

Angle and rotation

■ Use a protractor to measure and draw acute and obtuse angles to the nearest degree.

Resources

Provide each child with the following:
■ a copy of Activity 29 pupil sheet
■ a pencil
■ a protractor

Key words

degree   measure   angle   obtuse angle   acute angle   right angle   nearest

Say to the children:

Listen carefully.

I am going to tell you some things to do.

I will say them only once, so listen very carefully.

Do only the things you are told to do and nothing else.

If you make a mistake, cross it out. Do not use an eraser.

There are 11 parts to this activity.

The activity

1. Look at Box A. Measure the angle to the nearest degree. Write the answer in the circle.

2. Look at Box B. Measure the angle to the nearest degree. Write the answer in the circle.

3. In Box F draw an angle of 128 degrees.

4. In Box L draw an angle of 56 degrees.

5. Look at Box G. Measure the angle to the nearest degree. Write the answer in the circle.

6. In Box C draw an angle of 173 degrees.

7. Look at Box I. Measure the angle to the nearest degree. Write the answer in the circle.

8. Write your name in Box H.

9. In Box D draw an angle of 11 degrees.

10. Look at Box E. Measure the angle to the nearest degree. Write the answer in the circle.

11. In Box J draw an angle of 94 degrees.

Answers

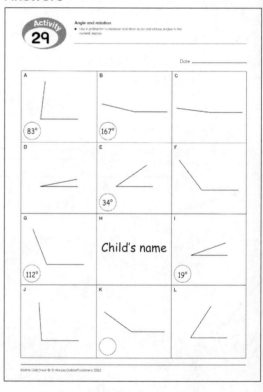

Discussion questions

↓ Which box has an angle of 34 degrees? (box E)

↓ How many degrees is the angle in box C? (173°)

■ How do you know if an angle is an obtuse/acute or right angle? (obtuse > 90°; acute < 90°; right angle = 90°)

■ Look at the angle in box A/B/C... Is it an acute/obtuse/right angle? (acute/obtuse/obtuse...)

↑ How do you know if an angle is a reflex angle? (greater than 180° and less than 360°)

↑ Which angle did you not measure? (K) Measure it now. What is the size of the angle? (145°)

Activity 29

Angle and rotation

■ Use a protractor to measure and draw acute and obtuse angles to the nearest degree.

Date _____

A 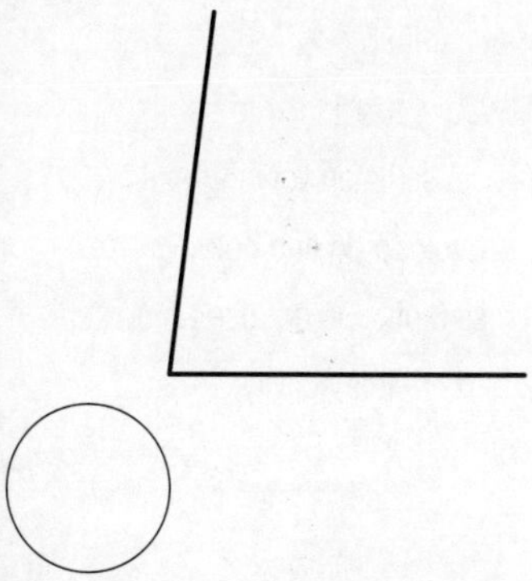	B 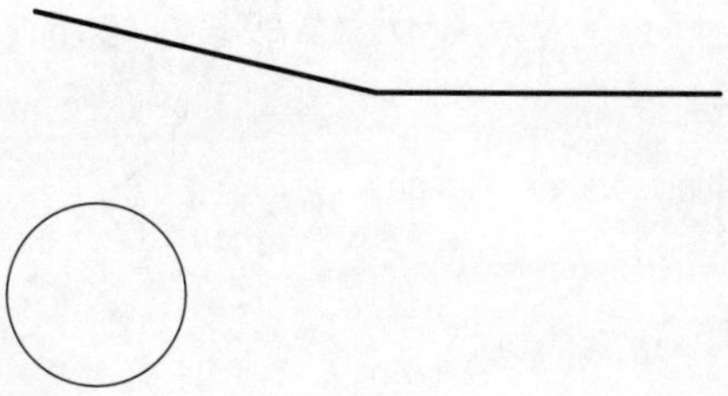	C
D	E 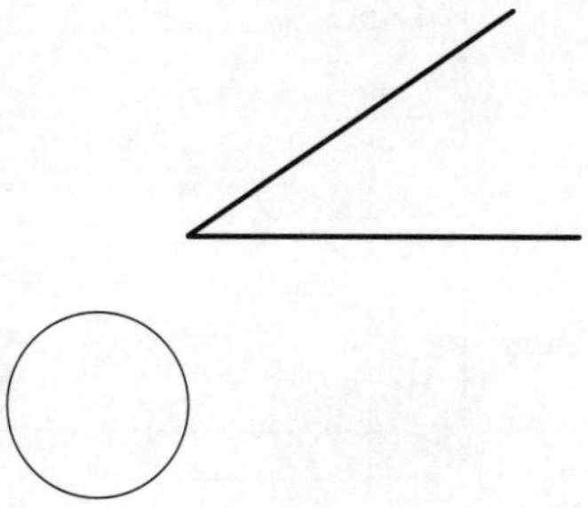	F
G 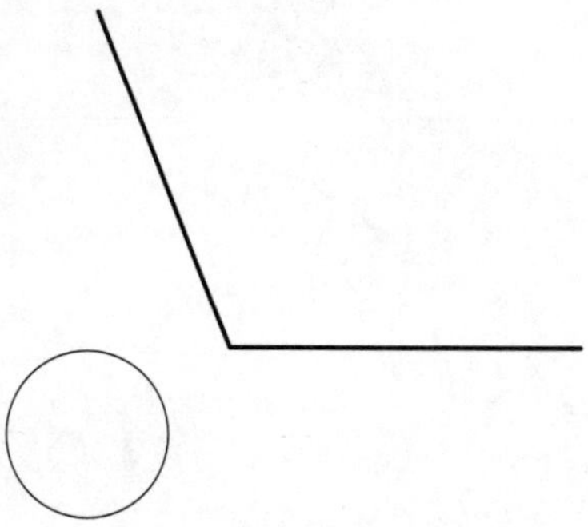	H	I 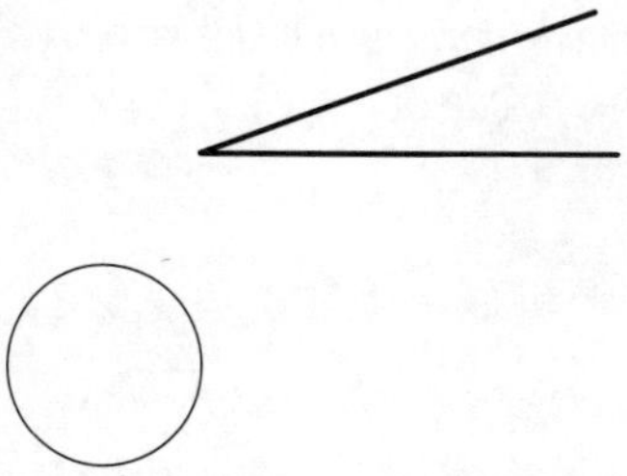
J	K 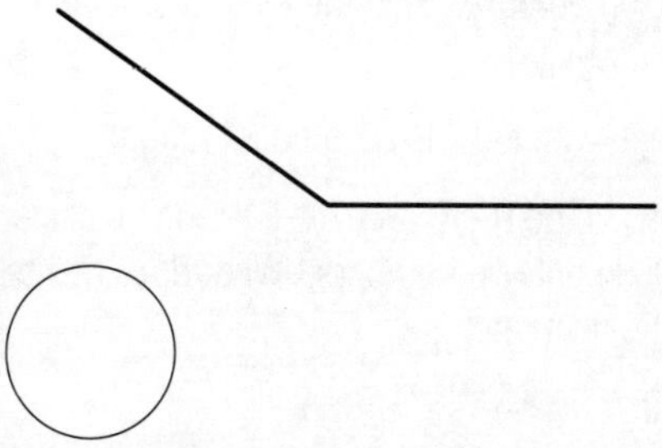	L

Maths Call (Year 6) © HarperCollins*Publishers* 2002

Handling data

■ Solve a problem by representing, extracting and interpreting data in bar charts with grouped discrete data.

Resources

Provide each child with the following:
■ a copy of Activity 30 pupil sheet
■ a coloured pencil

You will also need two 0 – 9 dice.

Key words

zero, one, two…one hundred   product   multiply   range   graph
bar chart   data   grouped data

Say to the children:

Listen carefully.

I am going to tell you some things to do.

I will say them only once, so listen very carefully.

Do only the things you are told to do and nothing else.

If you make a mistake, cross it out. Do not use an eraser.

There are 2 parts to this activity.

The activity

Note: Italicised instructions are for the teacher and are not to be read out to the children.

1. Write your name at the top of the sheet.

    This activity is about collecting and organising data in a bar chart where data is grouped.

    I am going to roll two dice and call out the numbers. You have to multiply the two numbers together.

2. When you have worked out the answer look along the bottom of the bar chart to find the product range that matches the answer (e.g. 7 times 5 equals 35 matches the product range 31 to 40). Then you colour just one box above that product range.

    Roll the two dice and call out the numbers.

    Continue until one product range has most of its boxes coloured.

Answers

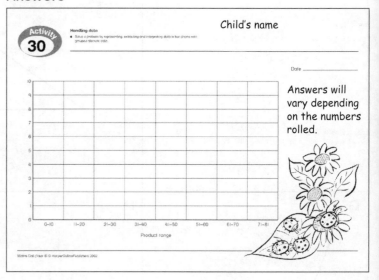

Answers will vary depending on the numbers rolled.

Discussion questions

↓ Which product range occurred the most/least?

↓ Which product range was thrown five/six/seven times?

■ The 31–40 product range has more/less coloured boxes than the 61–70 product range. How many more/less?

■ Compare for me the zero to ten product range with the 71–81 product range.

↑ What do you notice about the product ranges? (The 0–10 and 71–81 range include 11 numbers where all the other ranges include only 10 numbers.) What does this tell you about the results of the bar chart? (not 100% accurate)

↑ Tell me some statements about the bar chart.

Handling data

■ Solve a problem by representing, extracting and interpreting data in bar charts with grouped discrete data.

Date _____

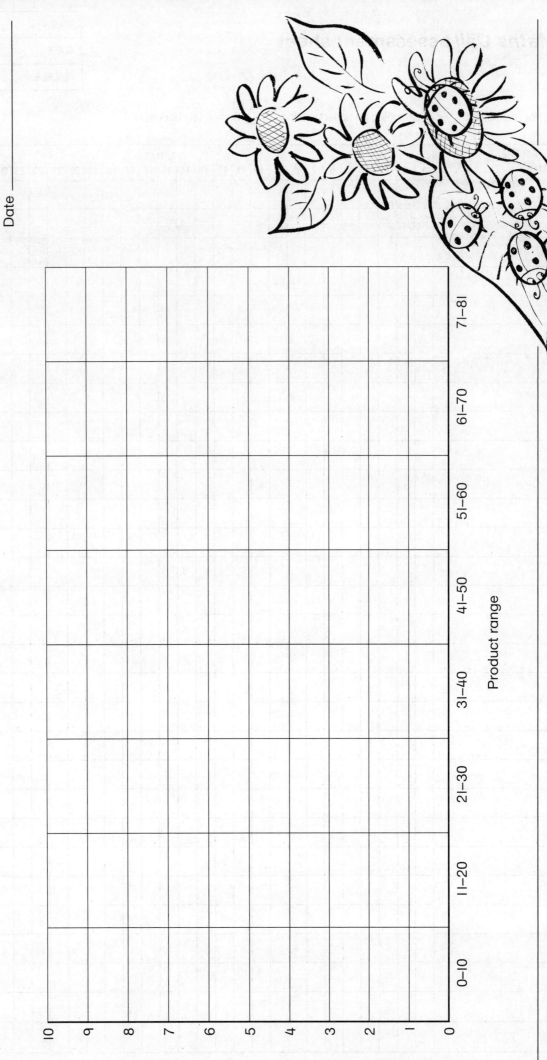

	0–10	11–20	21–30	31–40	41–50	51–60	61–70	71–81

Product range

(vertical axis: 10, 9, 8, 7, 6, 5, 4, 3, 2, 1, 0)

Maths Call assessment sheet

| YEAR |
| CLASS |
| TEACHER |

/ Not understood   ∠ Developing an understanding   △ Completely understood

NAME	ACTIVITY																													
	1	2	3	4	5	6	7	8	9	10	11	12	13	14	15	16	17	18	19	20	21	22	23	24	25	26	27	28	29	30